JUNIOR CERTIFI(

Science Revision

Shea Mullally

GILL EDUCATION

Gill Education

Hume Avenue

Park West

Dublin 12

www.gilleducation.ie

Gill Education is an imprint of M.H. Gill & Co.

© Shea Mullally 2011

978 07171 46970

Design by Liz White Designs

Artwork and print origination by MPS Limited, a Macmillan Company

The paper used in this book is made from the wood pulp of managed forests.
For every tree felled, at least one tree is planted, thereby renewing natural resources.

For permission to reproduce photographs, the author and publisher gratefully acknowledge the following:

© Getty Images: 3, 6R, 128, 141, 180; © Photolibrary: 104, 157; © Science Photo Library: 6L, 166.

The authors and publisher have made every effort to trace all copyright holders, but if any has been inadvertently overlooked we would be pleased to make the necessary arrangement at the first opportunity.

CONTENTS

Introduction v
Exam breakdown v
Previously examined topics by year vi
How to study viii
Your study plan ix
The examination xi

BIOLOGY 1
1. Living Things: Animals and Plants 2
2. Feeding and Digestion 8
3. Respiration and Breathing 18
4. Circulation of Blood 24
5. Excretion: Removal of Waste Products 28
6. The Skeleton 30
7. Sensitivity and Co-ordination 34
8. Reproduction 38
9. Genetics 43
10. Plant Structure and Transport in Plants 45
11. Photosynthesis and Tropisms 51
12. Plant Reproduction 55
13. Ecology and Habitat Study 60
14. Micro-organisms 69

CHEMISTRY 71
15. Elements, Compounds and Mixtures 72
16. The Periodic Table, Metals, Alkali and Alkaline Earth Metals 76
17. Solutions and Separating Mixtures 86
18. Air, Oxygen and Carbon Dioxide 95

19. Water 104

20. Atomic Structure, Ionic and Covalent Bonding 112

21. Acids and Bases 121

22. Fossil Fuels, Acid Rain and Plastics..127

PHYSICS **131**

23. Measurement, Density and Flotation...132

24. Speed, Velocity and Acceleration 138

25. Forces, Levers and Moments of a Force..141

26. Work, Power and Energy 150

27. Pressure 156

28. Heat and Temperature 163

29. Light...176

30. Sound...183

31. Magnetism 187

32. Static Electricity and Current Electricity..190

33. Electronics 201

Introduction

Exam breakdown

The Junior Certificate Science syllabus is divided into **three parts**: Coursework A, Coursework B and Coursework C (the written examination).

Part	Content	Marks	Per cent of total Junior Certificate Science marks
Coursework A	The **31 mandatory experiments and investigations** carried out in class over the course of three years	60	10
Coursework B	**Two specified** investigations **or one investigation of the student's own choice**, carried out in the third year	150	25
Coursework C	A **written examination** in Biology, Chemistry and Physics taken at the end of the third year	390	65
Total		600	100

> **Mandatory Experiments**
> The **mandatory experiments** throughout this book conform to the required State Examinations Commission standard for laboratory books. The required diagrams, procedures, calculations, results and conclusions can be duplicated or altered and entered into your laboratory book.

The written examination (Coursework C)

1. There are **three sections** in the paper. Each section has equal marks.
   - Biology (130 marks).
   - Chemistry (130 marks).
   - Physics (130 marks).
2. **Each section has three questions**: Biology (1, 2 and 3), Chemistry (4, 5 and 6) and Physics (7, 8 and 9).
3. Each of the three sections is **similar in structure**.
4. **All nine questions** must be answered in the answer book provided.
5. There is **no choice** of questions.

 Note: Material that is to be studied only by those taking Higher level is indicated in the text.

Section	Question 1 (52 marks)	Question 2	Question 3
Biology (1, 2, 3) Total marks = 130 Q.1 = (7 × 6 + 10) = 52 Q.2 = 39 Q.3 = 39	**Parts (a) to (h)** cover the entire Biology course. Parts (a) to (g) are short, simple questions (7 × 6 marks). Part (h) is a more detailed question (10 marks).	Question 2, like question 3, contains **two or three parts**, based on detailed **aspects of human and plant biology** and on the **mandatory experiments and investigations.**	Question 3 **is similar in style** to question 2. It is **usually based on habitats** and on the mandatory **experiments and investigations.**
	Question 4	**Question 5**	**Question 6**
Chemistry (4, 5, 6) Total marks = 130 Q.4 = (7 × 6 + 10) = 52 Q.5 = 39 Q.6 = 39	**Parts (a) to (h)** cover the entire Chemistry course. It has the same structure as questions 1 and 7.	Questions 5 and 6 usually contain **two or three parts** that require detailed answers. The questions are often based on the **mandatory experiments and investigations.**	**Question 6 is similar to question 5.**
	Question 7	**Question 8**	**Question 9**
Physics (7, 8, 9) Total marks = 130 Q.7 = (7 × 6 + 10) = 52 Q.8 = 39 Q.9 = 39	**Parts (a) to (h)** cover the entire Physics course. It has the same structure as questions 1 and 4.	Questions 8 and 9 usually contain **two or three parts** that require detailed answers. The questions are often based on the **mandatory experiments and investigations.**	**Question 9 is similar to question 8.**

Previously examined topics by year

The table on the following page indicates topics that were examined as **major parts** or as **full questions** in previous years. To some extent, it is possible to predict the topics that may be examined in a future year.

	Chapter	Examination topic	Examined in year(s)
BIOLOGY	1	Living Things: Animals and Plants	2006
	2	Feeding and Digestion	2006, 2007, 2008, 2010
	3	Respiration and Breathing	2006, 2007, 2009
	4	Circulation of Blood	2006
	5	Excretion: Removal of Waste Products	2008
	6	The Skeleton	2009
	7	Sensitivity and Co-ordination	
	8	Reproduction	2009
	9	Genetics	
	10	Plant Structure and Transport in Plants	
	11	Photosynthesis and Tropisms	2007, 2010
	12	Plant Reproduction	2007, 2010
	13	Ecology and Habitat Study	2006, 2007, 2008, 2009
	14	Micro-organisms	
CHEMISTRY	15	Elements, Compounds and Mixtures	2006
	16	The Periodic Table, Metals, Alkali and Alkaline Earth Metals	2006, 2009, 2010
	17	Solutions and Separating Mixtures	2006, 2007, 2009, 2010
	18	Air, Oxygen and Carbon Dioxide	2006, 2007, 2009
	19	Water	2006, 2007, 2009, 2010
	20	Atomic Structure, Ionic and Covalent Bonding	2006, 2008, 2009
	21	Acids and Bases	2006, 2007, 2010
	22	Fossil Fuels, Acid Rain and Plastics	2006
PHYSICS	23	Measurement, Density and Flotation	2009
	24	Speed, Velocity and Acceleration	2009
	25	Forces, Levers and Moments of a Force	2006, 2007, 2010
	26	Work, Power and Energy	2009, 2010
	27	Pressure	
	28	Heat and Temperature	2006, 2008, 2009, 2010
	29	Light	2006, 2009, 2010
	30	Sound	2007
	31	Magnetism	2010
	32	Static Electricity and Current Electricity	2006, 2007, 2008, 2009
	33	Electronics	2008, 2009

How to study

Successful study depends on study skills such as **good revision technique and good examination techniques**, but also on your own **individual skills**.

Revision

1. Set your **goals based on the aims** at the beginning of each chapter.
2. **Subdivide your goals into mini-goals:** Break up each task into smaller steps.
3. **Make out a timetable** (see the study plan that follows).
4. **Review your progress:** Do **quick mini-tests**, brainstorms and word dumps to see what you have learned, or more importantly, what you have forgotten.
5. **Tick off each completed goal:** This helps to build up your confidence.

Planning your study time

1. Study **during the day** – morning is best.
2. Thirty minutes is sufficient for intense study. Take a five-minute break and start again.
3. **Review (revise)** as soon as possible after class.
4. Be very **specific about when and what** you are going to study. This saves valuable time. For example:
   Time: 5.00–5.30 Tuesday   **Topic**: The digestive system

Learning in class

Try to develop some good habits before, during and after class.

Before class

1. **Review the previous material** covered in class.
2. **Scan** through the revision book and highlight any possible **difficulties** you might encounter. **Write them down**.

During class

1. **Be organised and concentrate** on what is going on. Do not talk or daydream.
2. **Listen actively** by looking out for key phrases from the teacher, such as, 'This is very important', 'It may come up in the examinations', etc.
3. Make a **note on the main points**, especially the ones that you have difficulty with.
4. **Make a note of where you found it difficult**. Hand it up to the teacher and ask for help.

After class

1. **Review** your notes and revision book within 24 hours.
2. Close the book and give yourself a five-minute **mini-test**.
3. Correct your **mistakes**.

Your study plan

1. Fill in the topic or part of each topic that you intend to revise.
2. Fill in the date on which you revised it.
3. Tick (√) when you are satisfied that you have revised it well.
4. Tick (√) when you have reviewed it. (Do a short test or mind map.)

BIOLOGY	Topics covered	Date	Revised	Reviewed again
1. Living Things: Animals and Plants				
2. Feeding and Digestion				
3. Respiration and Breathing				
4. Circulation of Blood				
5. Excretion: Removal of Waste Products				
6. The Skeleton				
7. Sensitivity and Co-ordination				
8. Reproduction				
9. Genetics				
10. Plant Structure and Transport in Plants				
11. Photosynthesis and Tropisms				
12. Plant Reproduction				
13. Ecology and Habitat Study				
14. Micro-organisms				

CHEMISTRY	Topics covered	Date	Revised	Reviewed again
15. Elements, Compounds and Mixtures				
16. The Periodic Table, Metals, Alkali and Alkaline Earth Metals				
17. Solutions and Separating Mixtures				
18. Air, Oxygen and Carbon Dioxide				
19. Water				
20. Atomic Structure, Ionic and Covalent Bonding				
21. Acids and Bases				
22. Fossil Fuels, Acid Rain and Plastics				

PHYSICS	Topics covered	Date	Revised	Reviewed again
23. Measurement, Density and Flotation				
24. Speed, Velocity and Acceleration				
25. Forces, Levers and Moments of a Force				
26. Work, Power and Energy				
27. Pressure				
28. Heat and Temperature				
29. Light				
30. Sound				
31. Magnetism				
32. Static Electricity and Current Electricity				
33. Electronics				

The examination

1. The paper is a two-hour examination.
2. Allow about five minutes to **read carefully through the entire paper**. This allows you to:
   - Highlight the key points in each question.
   - Decide what the easiest questions are.
3. Answer the **easy** questions first. This increases your **confidence** and also saves time for the more difficult questions.
4. Allow about ten minutes to read over the examination paper and your examination script at the end of the examination.
5. Allow about 35 minutes each for Biology, Chemistry and Physics.
6. Answer **all questions**. Do not leave any blank spaces – you may get marks for an attempted or guessed answer.
7. **Reread** through each question as you finish it. You may have misread the question or you may have left something out.
8. **Check through** all your answers at the end of the examination.
9. **Hand up** your paper. **Relax** – you have earned it.

BIOLOGY

1 Living Things: Animals and Plants

In this chapter you need to learn:

1. The basic life processes and the characteristics of living things.
2. Mandatory experiment: How to investigate the variety of plants and animals in their environment.
3. How to use a microscope.
4. How to compare animal and plant cells.
5. Mandatory experiment: Prepare a slide from plant tissue (onion) and sketch the cells under magnification.
6. All living things are made of cells.

What is biology?

Biology is the study of living things.

All living things (organisms) have certain common characteristics.

Basic life processes and characteristics of living things

- **Feeding:** All living things need food for energy. Plants make their own food, while animals eat plants and other animals for food.
- **Respiration:** All animals and plants release energy from food.
- **Movement and sensitivity:** Animals respond quickly to stimuli and can move about from place to place. Plants respond to stimuli like light, water and gravity by growing slowly towards the stimulus. For example, plants bend towards light.
- **Growth:** All living things grow.
- **Reproduction:** All living things reproduce, otherwise life would not exist.
- **Excretion:** All living things get rid of poisonous substances. This is called excretion.
- **Cells:** All living things are made of cells. Some organisms are made up of only one cell.

Mandatory experiment

Investigate the variety of living things by direct observation of animals and plants in their environment, classifying living organisms as animals or plants and animals as vertebrates or invertebrates

Woodland Visit
22 April 2011

Investigation by G. Hughes

Introduction

Animals that **have backbones** are called **vertebrates** (humans, cows, birds, etc.). Animals that have **no backbone** are called **invertebrates** (slugs, butterflies, spiders, etc.).

Procedure

1. The class group visited the woodland in Glen of the Downs outside Dublin.
2. The class made notes of all the living things that were seen.
3. The class looked at leaves, at the soil, under stones, in cracks in the ground and in cracks in trees.
4. The class took care not to disturb anything and tried to leave everything as we found it.
5. The class presented the results in the form of a table.

Results

Plants	Animals	
	Vertebrates	Invertebrates
Grass	Red squirrel	Wood louse
Moss	Grey squirrel	Millipede
Wild garlic	Robin	Butterfly
Wild woodbine	Wren	Spider
Oak	Mouse	
Birch		
Beech		

Studying cells

Biologists study cells using a microscope. The parts of a typical microscope are shown in the diagram below.

- **Eyepiece lens:** Look through this to see the object (animal or plant cells) being magnified.
- **Focusing knob:** This is used to lower and raise the stage. It brings the object into focus.
- **Objective lens:** The magnifying power can be changed by using different lenses.
- **Stage:** This is used to hold the glass slide and the object being magnified in position. A small opening allows light through.
- **Light source:** The light source may be an electric light bulb or may be natural light reflected through a mirror.

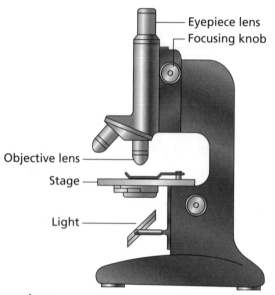

Comparison of plant and animal cells

Plant and animal cells have certain features in common with each other. They also have features that are different.

key point

All **living things** are made up of cells.

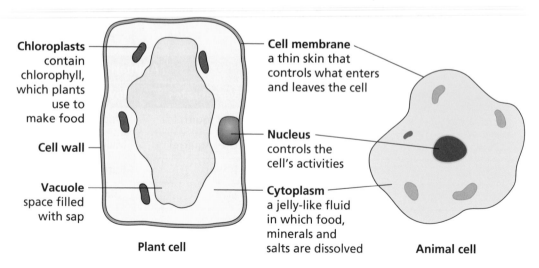

Chloroplasts contain chlorophyll, which plants use to make food

Cell wall

Vacuole space filled with sap

Cell membrane a thin skin that controls what enters and leaves the cell

Nucleus controls the cell's activities

Cytoplasm a jelly-like fluid in which food, minerals and salts are dissolved

Plant cell

Animal cell

Plant cells	Animal cells
Contain chloroplasts	Do not contain chloroplasts
Have a cell wall	Do not have a cell wall
Have large vacuoles	Some have temporary vacuoles

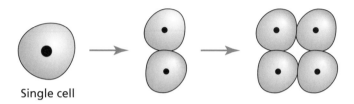

Single cell

A single cell divides into two parts. These can divide again and again. **Growth in animals and plants is a result of cell division.**

- **Tissues:** A tissue is a group of similar cells with a special function. Muscle cells, nerve cells and blood cells are examples of tissues.
- **Organs:** An organ is a group of tissues that work together to perform a special function. For example, a nose contains skin tissue, bone tissue and blood tissue. A leaf contains phloem and xylem tissue.
- **Systems:** A system is a group of organs working together. For example, the digestive system consists of the oesophagus, the stomach, the intestines and other organs.

Mandatory experiment

Prepare a slide from plant tissue (onion) and sketch the cells under magnification

Procedure

1. Place a drop of water in the centre of a glass slide. Add a drop of iodine.
2. Cut an onion open on a cutting board.
3. Use a forceps to peel away a small piece from one of the inner layers of the onion's skin.
4. Spread the onion skin onto the water on the slide.
5. Gently lower a cover slip over the onion tissue.
6. Examine the onion cells under high-power and low-power magnification.
7. Make a sketch of the onion cells.
8. Repeat the procedure but do not stain the cells with iodine.

Results

The nuclei are easier to see when the onion tissue is stained. The nuclei are orange-red in colour.

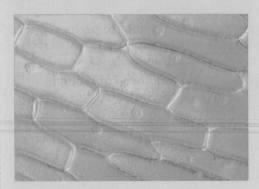
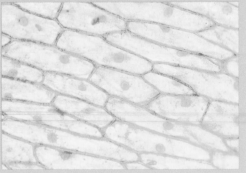

Nuclei of onion cells

Sample questions and answers

1. *Describe how to prepare a microscope slide from a plant tissue (onion).*

Answer

(i) Place a drop of water in the centre of a glass slide. Add a drop of iodine.

(ii) Cut an onion open on a cutting board.

(iii) Use a forceps to peel away a small piece from one of the inner layers of the onion's skin.

(iv) Spread the onion skin onto the water on the slide.

(v) Gently lower a cover slip over the onion tissue.

(vi) Examine the onion cells under high-power and low-power magnification.

2. *Draw a labelled diagram of a plant cell.*

Answer

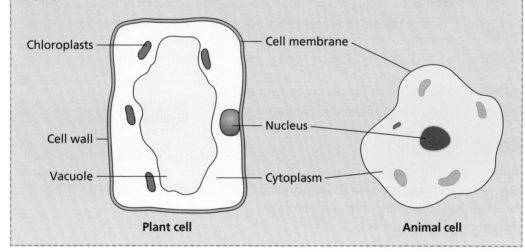

Chloroplasts

Cell membrane

Cell wall

Nucleus

Vacuole

Cytoplasm

Plant cell

Animal cell

2 Feeding and Digestion

In this chapter you need to learn:

1. The six constituents of a balanced diet and the source and function of each constituent.
2. The food pyramid.
3. Mandatory experiments to test for (a) starch (b) reducing sugars (c) protein (d) fat.
4. Mandatory experiment: Investigate the conversion of chemical energy in food to heat energy.
5. The processes involved in human nutrition.
6. The digestive system.
7. Enzymes.
8. Mandatory experiment: To investigate the action of amylase on starch.
9. Types of teeth and their structure.

All living things need food for energy, growth and repair, movement and protection from disease.

Balanced diet

In order to stay healthy, humans need a balanced diet. A balanced diet contains six constituents: carbohydrates (including fibre), fats, proteins, vitamins, minerals and water.

key point

A **balanced diet** contains the right amount of the food types essential for healthy living.

Type	Source	Function
Carbohydrate	Bread, potatoes and sugar	Quick release of energy
Protein	Meat, fish and vegetables	Growth and repair
Fat	Butter, oils and margarine	Slow release of energy
Vitamins	Vitamin C from oranges Vitamin D from milk	Vitamin C for healthy skin and gums Vitamin D for strong bones and teeth
Minerals	Calcium from milk and eggs Iron from spinach and liver	Calcium for strong bones and teeth Iron for making red blood cells
Water	Drinks and vegetables	Prevents dehydration
Fibre	Cereals and vegetables	Prevents constipation

The food pyramid

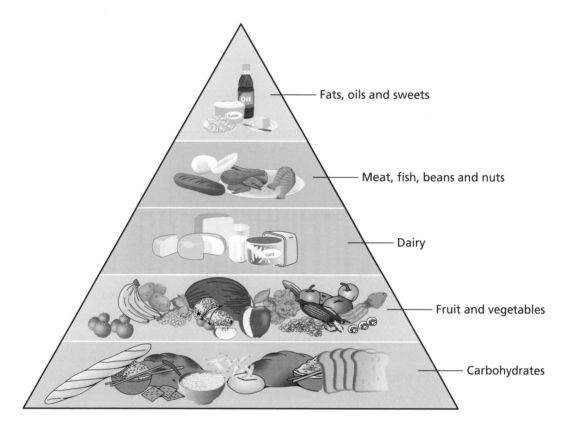

Fats, oils and sweets

Meat, fish, beans and nuts

Dairy

Fruit and vegetables

Carbohydrates

Level	Quantity eaten	Examples
Top	Smallest	Fats, sugars and confectionary
Second	Small	Meat, fish, beans and nuts
Third	Medium	Milk, butter, cheese and milk products
Fourth	Large	Fruit and vegetables
Bottom	Largest	Bread, pasta, cereals, rice and potatoes

Mandatory experiments

(a) To test for starch

Test for starch

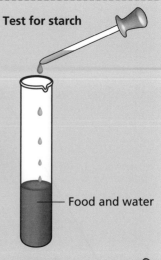

Procedure

1. Add some water to the food and mash it up into a paste.
2. Add iodine to the food.

Result

The food turns blue-black in colour.

— Food and water

(b) To test for reducing sugars

Test for glucose

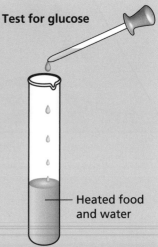

Procedure

1. Add some water to the food and mash it up into a paste.
2. Add Benedict's solution to the food.
3. Heat gently in a water bath.

Result

The food turns green and then orange-red.

— Heated food and water

(c) To test for proteins (Biuret test)

Test for protein

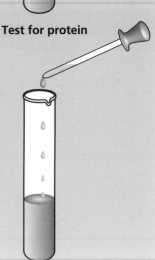

Procedure

1. Add some water to the food and mash it up into a paste.
2. Add some 10 per cent sodium hydroxide solution.
3. Add some drops of copper (II) sulphate solution.
4. Heat gently.

Result

The food turns violet in colour.

(d) To test for fats

Test for fats

Procedure
1. Squeeze food in a piece of brown paper.
2. Leave to dry.

Result
A translucent spot appears.

Food	Procedure	Result
Starch	Add iodine to food.	Food turns blue-black.
Reducing sugars (glucose)	Add Benedict's solution to the food. Heat gently.	Solution turns green, then orange-red.
Proteins	Add sodium hydroxide solution to food. Add copper sulphate solution. Heat gently.	Solution turns violet.
Fats	Squeeze food in greaseproof paper.	A translucent spot appears.

Energy in food

Most food packets give details of the energy available in the various food products. For example, the information on the packet shown here tells us that each **100 g of the food provides us with 1580 kJ of energy**. The nutrition information also gives us details of the amounts of the different food types in the packet. This particular one tells us that there is 7 g of protein, 0.95 g of sodium, etc.

Ingredients

Maize, Sugar, Barley Malt Flavouring, Salt, Glucose-Fructose Syrup, Niacin, Iron, Vitamin B$_6$, Riboflavin (B$_2$), Thiamin (B$_1$), Folic Acid, Vitamin B$_{12}$.

Guideline Daily Amounts

EACH DAY	WOMEN	MEN
Calories	2000	2500
Fat	70 g	95 g

'Official Government figures for average adults'

Nutrition Information

◯ Typical value per 100 g   ◯ 30 g serving with 125 ml of semi-skimmed milk

	Typical value per 100 g	30 g serving with 125 ml of semi-skimmed milk
ENERGY	1580 kJ 372 kcal	726 kJ 171 kcal
PROTEIN	7 g	6 g
CARBOHYDRATES	84 g	32 g
of which sugars	8 g	9 g
starch	76 g	23 g
FAT	0.9 g	2.5 g
of which saturates	0.2 g	1.5 g
FIBRE	3 g	0.9 g
SODIUM	0.95 g	0.35 g
VITAMINS:	(% RDA)	(% RDA)
THIAMIN (B$_1$)	1.2 mg (85)	0.4 mg (30)
RIBOFLAVIN (B$_2$)	1.3 mg (85)	0.6 mg (40)
NIACIN	15 mg (85)	4.6 mg (25)
VITAMIN B$_6$	1.7 mg (85)	0.6 mg (30)
FOLIC ACID	167 μg (85)	60 μg (30)
VITAMIN B$_{12}$	0.85 μg (85)	0.75 μg (75)
MINERALS:		
IRON	7.9 mg (55)	2.4 mg (17)

Mandatory experiment

Investigate the conversion of chemical energy in food to heat energy

Procedure

1. Carefully clamp a test tube to a retort stand.
2. Fill it about two-thirds full with water.
3. Place a thermometer in the test tube.
4. Light the peanut (or any other food rich in energy) with a Bunsen burner.
5. Hold it under the test tube.
6. The temperature of the water in the test tube rises.

Conclusion

Foods contain chemical energy that can be converted to heat energy.

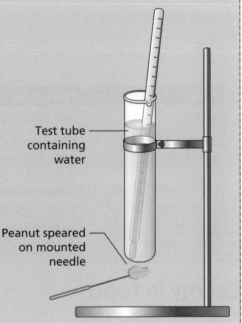

Test tube containing water

Peanut speared on mounted needle

Feeding: nutrition

Feeding in humans and most other animals involves the following processes.

- **Ingestion:** Food is taken into the mouth.
- **Digestion:** Food is broken up into soluble substances by the teeth and by digestive enzymes.
- **Absorption:** Soluble substances are absorbed into the bloodstream.
- **Assimilation:** The soluble products of digestion are reorganised and used for growth of new cells, for energy and to repair tissues and organs.
- **Egestion:** Undigested material is eliminated (excreted) through the anus.

The digestive system

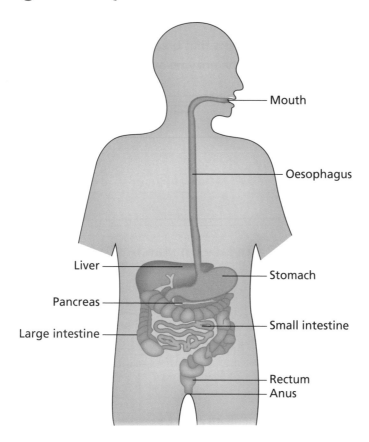

Mouth

Oesophagus

Liver

Stomach

Pancreas

Large intestine

Small intestine

Rectum

Anus

Food has to be broken up into smaller pieces before the body can use it. Food is broken up physically by the teeth and is broken up chemically by digestive enzymes. Carbohydrates are broken up into glucose, proteins are broken up into amino acids and fats are broken up into fatty acids and glycerol.

1. **Mouth:** Food is broken up and mixed with saliva. Saliva is an enzyme that breaks down carbohydrates.
2. **Oesophagus:** Food is pushed from the mouth to the stomach by muscular action called **peristalsis.**
3. **Stomach:** Food is acidified and digestive enzymes are added which break up the food.
4. **Liver:** Produces bile, which breaks down fats.
5. **Pancreas:** Produces digestive enzymes.
6. **Small intestine:** Digestive enzymes are added from the **pancreas**. Most of the digestion takes place in the small intestine. Nutrients are absorbed into the blood from the small intestine. The enzyme amylase breaks starch into maltose. Maltose is then broken up by the enzyme maltase into glucose.
7. **Large intestine:** Water is taken back into the body. Solid waste is stored before being egested through the anus.

key point

Digestive enzymes are biological catalysts that break down food.

Starch (substrate) is broken down by the enzyme amylase into a product, a sugar called maltose.

$$\text{starch} \quad \overset{\text{amylase}}{\Rightarrow} \quad \text{maltose}$$

exam focus

Mandatory experiment

To investigate the action of amylase on starch

Procedure

1. Add starch solution to a depth of 2 cm to each test tube.

2. Add saliva to test tube A, but not to B. Saliva contains the enzyme salivary amylase.

3. Place both test tubes in a water bath at 37°C for 15 to 20 minutes.

4. Use iodine to test B (no saliva) for starch. It turns blue-black.

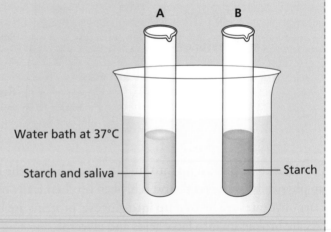

Water bath at 37°C

Starch and saliva

Starch

5. Use Benedict's solution to test A for glucose. It turns red-orange.

Result

Amylase present in saliva breaks starch into glucose.

End products of digestion

Food type	End products of digestion
Carbohydrate	Simple sugars
Protein	Amino acids
Fats	Fatty acids and glycerol

Types of teeth

An adult has 32 teeth – 16 in the upper jaw and 16 in the lower jaw.

- **Incisors** are sharp for cutting food.
- **Canines** are cone shaped for tearing food.
- **Premolars** are broad and bumpy for crushing food.
- **Molars** are large, broad and bumpy for crushing food.

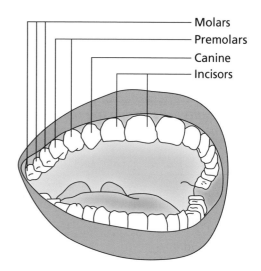

Molars
Premolars
Canine
Incisors

Tooth structure

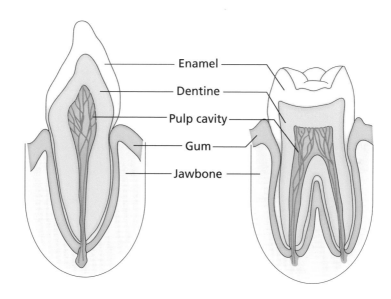

Enamel
Dentine
Pulp cavity
Gum
Jawbone

- **Enamel** is the hard, non-living protective coating.
- **Dentine** is the soft living part.
- The **pulp cavity** contains living cells, nerves and blood.
- **Cement** holds the root firmly in place.

Sample questions and answers

1. *Tests were carried out on three foods by a pupil in a school laboratory. The results are given in the table below. A + sign means a positive test and a − means a negative test. (Junior Cert 2006, Q3a (iii))*

Food tested	Food tests			
	Starch	Reducing sugar	Protein	Fat
Food A	+	−	−	+
Food B	−	−	+	+
Food C	+	−	+	+

(a) *Which of the foods A, B or C would most likely be cheese, meat or fish?*

Answer

Food B: Cheese, meat and fish contain protein and fat.

(b) *Which of the foods A, B or C would most likely be crisps or chips?*

Answer

Food A: Crisps and chips contain starch and fat.

2. *The diagram shows the human digestive system. (Junior Cert 2007, Q2b)*

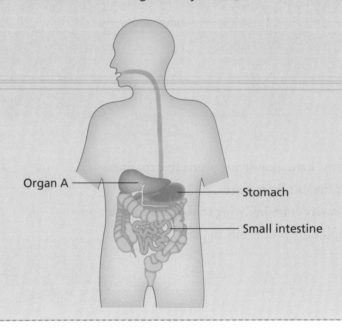

(a) *Give the name and a digestive function of organ A.*

Answer

The liver produces bile, which breaks down fats.

(b) *Starch is broken down in the small intestine by an enzyme. Name the enzyme and the sugar that the starch is broken down into.*

Answer

The enzyme amylase breaks starch into maltose.

(c) *Give a function of the small intestine other than digestion.*

Answer

Absorption of food, transport of materials.

3 Respiration and Breathing

aims **In this chapter you need to learn:**

1. The word equation for respiration.
2. The breathing system.
3. Gas exchange in the alveoli.
4. The products of aerobic respiration: carbon dioxide, water and heat.
5. Mandatory experiment: To compare the carbon dioxide levels of inhaled and exhaled air.

Respiration

Respiration is a characteristic of all animal and plant cells.

The word equation for respiration is:

$$\text{glucose} + \text{oxygen} \rightarrow \text{carbon dioxide} + \text{water} + \text{energy}$$

Aerobic respiration requires the presence of oxygen.

key point

Respiration is the release of energy from food (usually glucose).

Breathing

Humans breathe by exchanging oxygen for carbon dioxide in the lungs. Fish breathe by extracting oxygen from water in their gills.

Breathing is the process by which animals bring air or water into contact with their gaseous exchange surface.

The breathing system

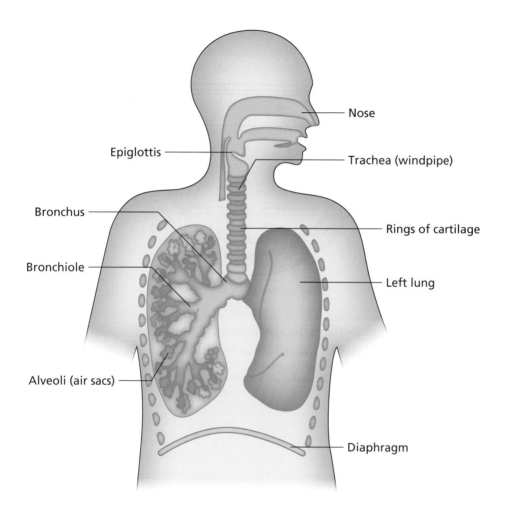

- **Nose:** Moistens, cleans and tests the air taken in.
- **Epiglottis:** Stops food from going down the lungs.
- **Trachea (windpipe):** Tube by which air is moved into and out of the lungs.
- **Rings of cartilage:** Keep the trachea permanently open.
- **Bronchus:** Carries air from the trachea to and from the lungs.
- **Bronchiole:** Narrow tubes through which gases diffuse to and from the alveoli.
- **Alveoli (air sacs):** Tiny air sacs through which gas exchange takes place via the blood capillaries. The large number ensures that there is a large surface area for gas exchange.
- **Diaphragm:** A strip of muscle that forces the air to move into and out of the lungs.

Gas exchange in the alveoli

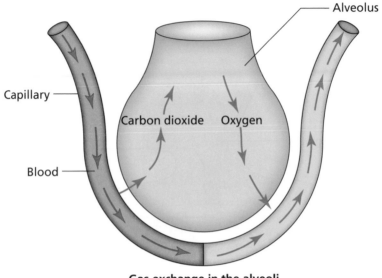

Gas exchange in the alveoli

Oxygen passes through the walls of the alveoli and into the blood capillaries by **diffusion.** Carbon dioxide passes the other way by diffusion.

Smoking damages your lungs – it makes breathing difficult and causes lung diseases, including cancer.

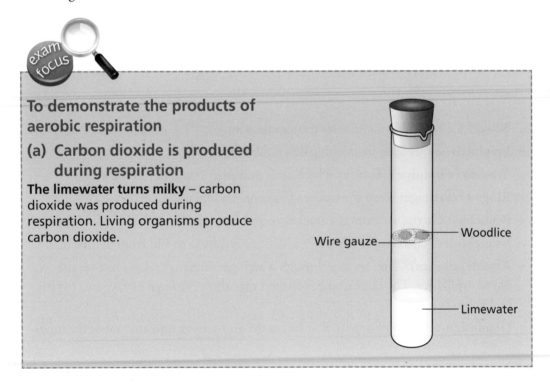

To demonstrate the products of aerobic respiration

(a) Carbon dioxide is produced during respiration

The limewater turns milky – carbon dioxide was produced during respiration. Living organisms produce carbon dioxide.

(b) Water is produced during respiration

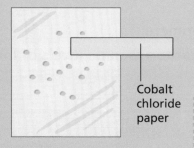

Cobalt chloride paper

The products of aerobic respiration are carbon dioxide, water and heat.

Procedure

1. Breathe onto a small piece of glass.
2. Drops of liquid form.
3. The liquid turns blue cobalt chloride paper pink.

> The use of cobalt chloride paper to test for water is being discontinued on health and safety grounds. It will still be used in examination questions. Anhydrous copper sulphate should be used instead to test for water. When water drops fall on anhydrous copper sulphate it turns blue.

Water was produced during respiration.

(c) Heat is produced during respiration

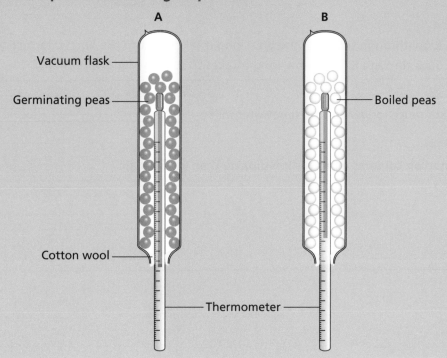

A   B

Vacuum flask

Germinating peas

Boiled peas

Cotton wool

Thermometer

The temperature rises in A but not in B – **heat was produced during respiration.**

Mandatory experiment

To compare the carbon dioxide levels of inhaled and exhaled air

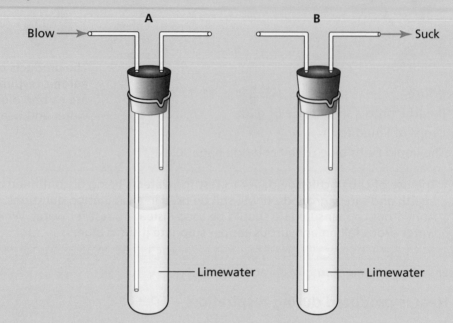

Procedure

1. Blow through tube A. Time how long it takes to turn the limewater milky.
2. Suck through B. Time how long it takes to turn the limewater milky.

Result

B takes much longer to turn limewater milky.

Conclusion

Expired air contains more carbon dioxide than inspired air.

Sample questions and answers

1. *The diagram shows the apparatus used by a pupil when performing an experiment in a school laboratory. The pupil blew (exhaled) air into tube X. The pupil sucked (inhaled) air from test tube Y. The pupil continued alternately blowing and sucking air until liquid A in one of the test tubes turned milky. (Junior Cert 2009, Q2b)*

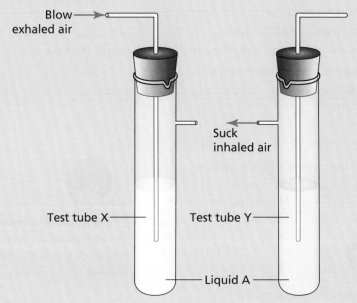

(a) *Name the liquid A.*

Answer

Limewater.

(b) *In which test tube, X or Y, did the liquid turn milky?*

Answer

Test tube X.

(c) *Why did the liquid turn milky in one of the test tubes?*

Answer

Carbon dioxide produced during respiration was blown into the limewater.

(d) *What conclusion can be made from the result of this experiment regarding the difference in composition between exhaled air and inhaled air?*

Answer

Exhaled air contains more carbon dioxide than inhaled air.

(e) *Write a word equation for anaerobic respiration.*

Answer

glucose + oxygen → carbon dioxide + water + energy

4 Circulation of Blood

aims In this chapter you need to learn:
1. The composition of blood.
2. The functions of blood.
3. Blood vessels.
4. The structure of the heart.
5. The circulatory system (flow of blood through the heart).
6. Breathing and pulse rate.
7. Heart disease.

Dissolved foods, hormones, oxygen, carbon dioxide, unwanted wastes and water are all transported around the body by blood.

Blood is a fluid consisting of blood cells and platelets suspended in a solution called plasma.

Circulation is the movement of blood around the body.

Composition of blood

- **Plasma** contains water, dissolved proteins, salts, hormones, antibodies and urea.
- **Platelets** clot blood.
- **White blood cells** protect against disease by engulfing germs or by releasing antibodies that kill germs.
- **Red blood cells** are cells without a nucleus. They contain haemoglobin, which is the substance that carries the oxygen.

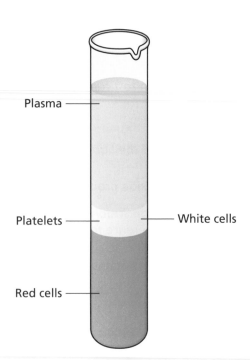

Plasma

Platelets — — White cells

Red cells

Functions of the blood

- **Absorbs** the products of digestion (food).
- **Circulates** food, oxygen, hormones, antibodies, carbon dioxide and unwanted substances like urea around the body.
- **Protects** against loss of fluid by clotting and also against disease by killing germs.
- **Controls** the amounts of water and chemicals in the tissues.
- **Regulates** body temperature. Normal body temperature is 37°C. Illness may cause a change in body temperature.

Blood vessels

- **Arteries** carry blood away from the heart to the body (cells and tissues). They carry blood under high pressure. They have thick muscular walls.
- **Veins** carry blood from the body back to the heart. They carry blood under low pressure. They have thinner walls and are wider than arteries. They have **valves** to prevent the blood flowing backwards.
- **Capillaries** are tiny and carry blood in and out through the tissues. They have very thin walls.

The structure of the heart

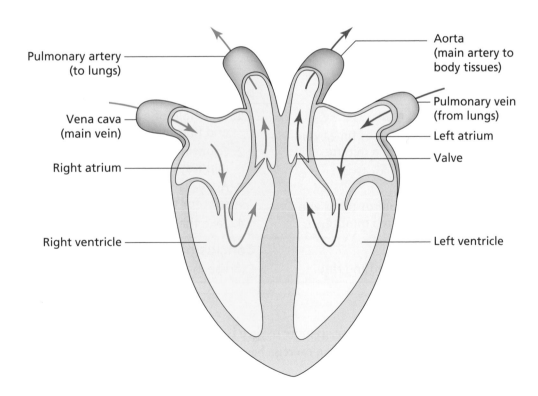

Pulmonary artery (to lungs)

Vena cava (main vein)

Right atrium

Right ventricle

Aorta (main artery to body tissues)

Pulmonary vein (from lungs)

Left atrium

Valve

Left ventricle

The circulatory system – the flow of blood through the heart

- The **heart** pumps blood around the body. It is a double pump.
- The heart is divided into **two sections** so that blood does not flow directly from one side to the other.

- The **vena cava** carries blood low in oxygen from the body into the heart.
- The **right atrium** has thin walls. It pumps oxygen into the right ventricle.
- The **right ventricle** has thicker walls because it pumps blood to the lungs.
- The **pulmonary artery** carries the low-oxygen blood to the lungs.
- The **pulmonary vein** carries blood rich in oxygen from the lungs to the heart.
- The **aorta** carries the oxygen-rich blood all around the body.
- The **left atrium** has thin walls. It pumps oxygen-rich blood into the left ventricle.
- The **left ventricle** has very thick walls because it pumps oxygen-rich blood all around the body.

Breathing rate and pulse rate

key point

A **pulse** is a heartbeat (pumping of blood) caused by changes in blood pressure in an artery.

Breathing rate

1. Sit down and relax.
2. Count the number of times you breathe in within a minute.
3. Run on the spot for two minutes.
4. Count the number of times you breathe in within a minute.

Conclusion

Exercise increases breathing rate.

Pulse rate

1. Take hold of a friend's wrist and find their pulse.
2. Count the number of beats per minute.
3. Ask your friend to run on the spot for two minutes.
4. Take their pulse again.

Conclusion

Exercise increases pulse rate.

Pulse rate increases with exercise, as more oxygen is required. The rate slows down when exercise has stopped, as less oxygen is required.

key point

The average pulse rate for an adult at rest is 70 beats per minute.

Heart disease

Heart disease can be prevented by:

- Regular exercise.
- Healthy diet.
- Not smoking.

Sample questions and answers

1. *Name and give the function of the four components of the blood.*

Answer

(i)   Red blood cells contain haemoglobin, which is the substance that carries the oxygen.

(ii) White blood cells protect against disease by engulfing germs or by releasing antibodies that kill germs.

(iii) Platelets clot blood.

(iv) Plasma contains water, dissolved proteins, salts, hormones, antibodies and urea.

2. *What are the main differences between arteries and veins?*

Answer

Arteries carry blood from the heart to the body. They have thick muscular walls.

Veins carry blood from the body back to the heart. They have thinner and wider walls than arteries.

5 Excretion: Removal of Waste Products

In this chapter you need to learn:

1. What is excretion?
2. The excretory organs: the lungs, skin and kidneys.
3. The structure of the urinary system.

Humans produce waste products such as carbon dioxide and urea during the day and at night. These waste products are the result of chemical reactions occurring in the cells of the body. These products are often poisonous and must be removed.

key point

Excretion is the removal of waste products produced during cell reactions from the body.

Excretory organs: The lungs, skin and kidneys

- **Lungs:** Carbon dioxide and water vapour produced during respiration are exhaled from the lungs.
- **Skin:** Sweat (water, salts and urea) is released via the sweat glands in skin. The sweat released cools the body by evaporation.
- **Kidneys:** Blood is carried to the kidneys, where it is filtered to remove waste products in the form of urine (water and urea). Urine is stored in the bladder and passed out through the urethra.
- **Ureters:** Carry urine from kidney to bladder.
- **Urethra:** A tube that carries urine from the bladder out of the kidneys.
- **Renal vein:** Purified blood is carried away from the kidneys.
- **Renal artery:** Carries blood and waste to the kidneys.

Organ	Waste product
Lungs (see Chapter 3)	CO_2 and H_2O
Skin	Sweat
Kidneys	Urine

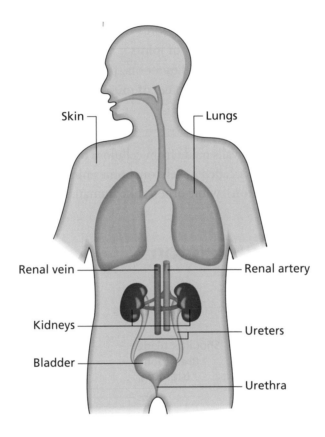

Sample questions and answers

1. *What is the difference between the renal vein and the renal artery?*

Answer

The renal vein carries purified blood away from the kidneys. The renal artery carries blood and waste to the kidneys.

2. *Name a function of sweat, other than excretion.*

Answer

Sweat helps to cool the body by evaporation.

6 The Skeleton

aims **In this chapter you need to learn:**
1. The functions of the skeleton.
2. The main bones of the skeleton.
3. Joints and different types of joints.
4. The differences between ligaments, tendons and cartilage.
5. Muscles and antagonistic pairs of muscles.

Animal cells do not have cell walls made from cellulose to support them. Animal cells are supported by a framework called a skeleton. Some animals, like lobsters, have an external skeleton (**exoskeleton**), while others, like humans, have an internal skeleton (**endoskeleton**).

Functions of the skeleton

- **Supports** the body and maintains its shape.
- **Protects** soft organs (brain, heart, lungs).
- **Makes red blood cells** in the bone marrow.
- **Enables us to move with the help of muscles.**

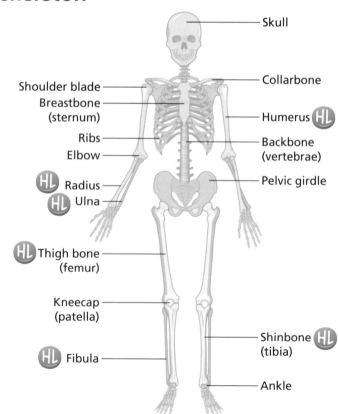

Skull

Collarbone

Shoulder blade

Breastbone (sternum)

Humerus **HL**

Ribs

Backbone (vertebrae)

Elbow

HL Radius

Pelvic girdle

HL Ulna

HL Thigh bone (femur)

Kneecap (patella)

Shinbone **HL** (tibia)

HL Fibula

Ankle

Joints (synovial)

- **Cartilage** is soft skeletal tissue that acts as a shock absorber between bones.
- **Synovial fluid** lubricates the joints and allows the bones to move easily.
- **Ligaments** connect bone to bone. They are elastic and can be stretched.
- **Tendons** connect muscles to bones. They have little elasticity and cannot be stretched.

A **joint** is the place where two bones move against each other.

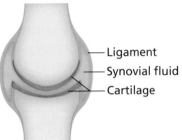

Ligament

Synovial fluid

Cartilage

Different types of joints

Ball and socket joints allow movement in all directions, e.g. hips, shoulder.

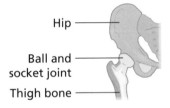

Hip

Ball and socket joint

Thigh bone

Hinge joints can bend in one direction only, e.g. knee, elbow.

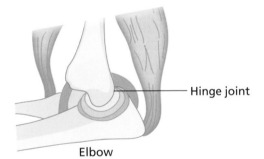

Hinge joint

Elbow

Fused joints have no movement, e.g. skull and pelvis.

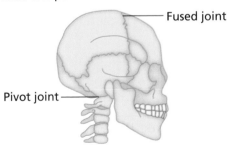

Fused joint

Pivot joint

Muscles

Bones are moved by the **contraction** of muscles. Another muscle is usually used to return the bone to its original position. For this reason, muscles usually occur in antagonistic pairs, which exert opposite forces.

> **key point**
>
> HL
>
> **Antagonistic muscles** are arranged in pairs in such a way that when they contract, they produce opposite effects, e.g. bending and straightening the arm.

Bending the forearm

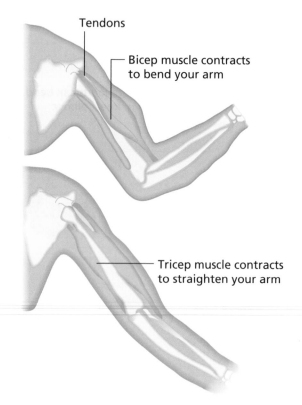

Tendons

Bicep muscle contracts to bend your arm

Tricep muscle contracts to straighten your arm

The arm is raised when the bicep contracts and the tricep relaxes. The arm is lowered when the bicep relaxes and the tricep contracts.

Sample questions and answers

1. *The diagram shows a human skeleton with a detailed drawing of the knee joint. The kneecap is not shown. (Junior Cert 2009, Q2a)*

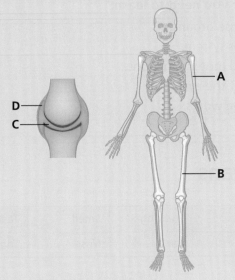

(a) *Name the main functions of the skeleton.*

Answer

Supports the body, protects soft organs, makes red blood cells, enables us to move with the help of muscles.

(b) *Name the bones labelled A and B.*

Answer

A = humerus.

B = femur (thigh bone).

(c) *What type of joint is the knee?*

Answer

Hinge joint.

(d) *C is synovial fluid. D is a ligament. What are the functions of the parts labelled C and D?*

Answer

C lubricates the joints and allows them to move more freely. D connects bone to bone. Ligaments are elastic and can be stretched.

(e) *How do antagonistic muscles work?*

Answer

Antagonistic muscles are arranged in pairs in such a way that when they contract, they produce opposite effects, e.g. bending and straightening the arm.

7 Sensitivity and Co-ordination

In this chapter you need to learn:

1. The five sense organs.
2. The nervous system.
3. Sensory and motor functions.
4. The parts of the eye.
5. How the eye works.

The sense organs

Sense	Sight	Hearing	Smell	Taste	Touch
Sense organ	Eye	Ear	Nose	Tongue	Skin

The nervous system

The nervous system consists of the **central nervous system** (the **brain** and the **spinal cord**) and the **peripheral nerves** (nerves connected to the brain and the spinal cord).

Nerves are made up of millions of nerve cells, called **neurons**. Messages travel very quickly along neurons as tiny electrical pulses.

The **function of the nervous system is** to transmit messages rapidly to all parts of the body and to co-ordinate the body's response.

- **Sensory nerves** carry messages from the sense organ to the brain.
- **Motor nerves** carry messages from the brain to the sense organ.

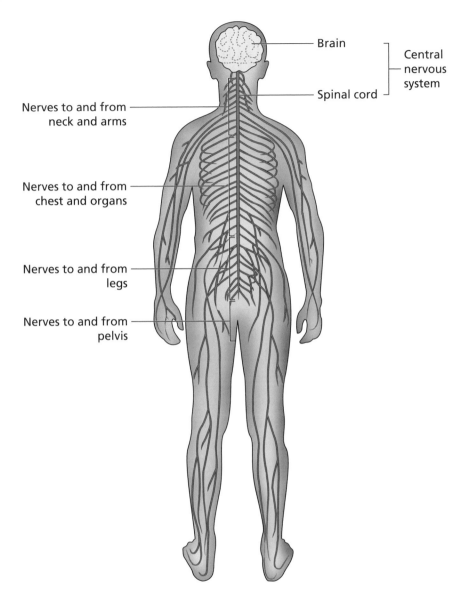

Brain

Central
nervous
system

Spinal cord

Nerves to and from
neck and arms

Nerves to and from
chest and organs

Nerves to and from
legs

Nerves to and from
pelvis

Sensory and motor functions

The sense organ receives a **stimulus**. A message is sent from the sense organ to the brain or spinal cord via a **sensory nerve**. The brain or spinal cord decides what to do, then sends a message along the **motor nerves** to the muscles and glands.

The eye

The eye is a sense organ made up of receptors that receive light stimuli. The eyes are located in the cranium. An optic nerve connects the eye to the brain.

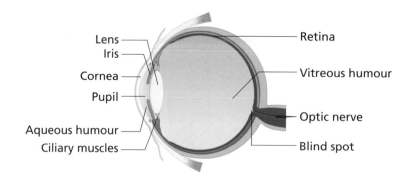

- The **cornea** bends (refracts) light rays.
- **Ciliary muscles** change the shape of the lens.
- The **iris** controls the amount of light entering the eye.
- The **lens** focuses light on the retina.
- The **pupil** is the black circle that allows light into the eye.
- **Vitreous humour** keeps the eyeball in a spherical shape.
- The **retina** contains light-sensitive cells.
- The **blind spot** contains no light-sensitive cells.

How does the eye work?

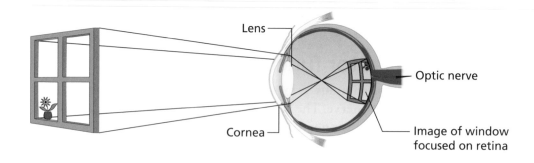

Light rays are bent (refracted) into the eye by the cornea and lens. An image is formed on the retina. The light-sensitive cells in the retina send a message along the optic nerve to the brain, which produces an image.

Sample questions and answers

1. (a) *Give the function of (i) the iris and (ii) the pupil. (Junior Cert 2008, Q1h)*

Answer

The iris controls the amount of light entering the eye, controls the size of the pupil and controls the brightness of the image on the retina.

The pupil allows light to enter the eye.

(b) *The pupil is transparent. Why does it appear to be black in most situations?*

Answer

Light is absorbed, no light is reflected.

2. *Nerves carry electrical messages around our bodies. Nerves have <u>motor functions</u> and <u>sensory functions</u>. Explain the meaning of the underlined terms.*

Answer

Motor functions: The brain (spinal cord or central nervous system) sends a message along the motor nerves to the muscles and glands.

Sensory function: The sense organ receives a stimulus. A message is sent from a sense organ to the brain (spinal cord or central nervous system) via a sensory nerve.

8 Reproduction

Sexual reproduction

The male produces a male sex cell (gamete) called a **sperm**. Sperm are produced in the **testes**.

The female produces a female sex cell (gamete) called an **egg (ovum)**. Eggs are produced in the **ovaries**.

key point

Sexual reproduction is the production of offspring by a male and a female.

key point

The fusion of the sperm with the egg is called **fertilisation**.

key point

The production of eggs is called **ovulation**.

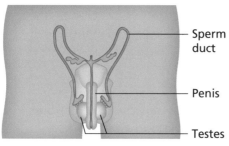

— Sperm duct

— Penis

— Testes

Male reproductive organs

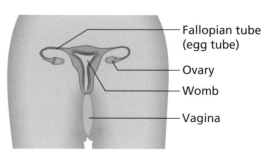

— Fallopian tube (egg tube)

— Ovary

— Womb

— Vagina

Female reproductive organs

What happens during reproduction?

1. **Sexual intercourse** takes place when the man inserts his penis into the woman's vagina.
2. **Insemination** occurs when the sperm is released into the vagina.
3. The sperm travel from the vagina up through the womb and **into the fallopian tubes.**
4. If a fertile egg is present, the sperm may **fertilise** the egg. At this stage the woman is **pregnant**.
5. **The male gamete fuses (joins) with the female gamete to produce a new cell called a zygote.**
6. This fertilised egg starts to **subdivide** into more and more cells.

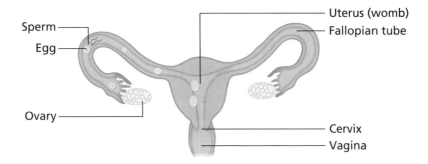

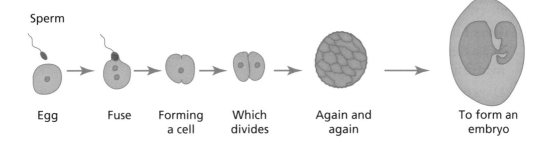

| Egg | Fuse | Forming a cell | Which divides | Again and again | To form an embryo |

7. This group of cells, called an embryo, moves down the fallopian tube and is **implanted** (attached) into the soft lining of the womb. During the next **36 weeks** or so, the embryo develops.
8. The **umbilical cord** connects the embryo to the placenta. The **placenta** is a filter that allows food and oxygen to pass from the mother to the embryo and carbon dioxide and other wastes to pass from the embryo to the mother.
9. **Birth** occurs some time after the **amnion** (water sac) bursts. The baby usually comes out head first. The umbilical cord is cut and the placenta (afterbirth) comes out. Milk is produced in the breasts to feed the baby.

The menstrual cycle

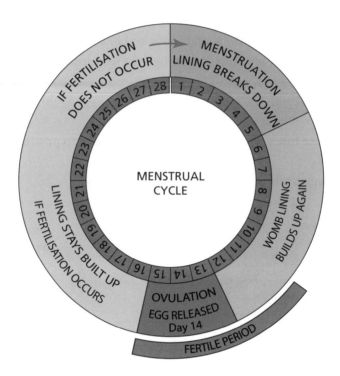

A woman's body goes through a series of changes every **28 days** or so in preparation for pregnancy.

- **Days 1 to 5:** When the woman is not pregnant, the lining of the womb breaks down for the first five days or so and passes out of the body. This is called **menstruation**.
- **Days 6 to 13:** A new lining then starts to build up again in preparation for a possible pregnancy.
- **Day 14: Ovulation occurs.**
- **Days 11 to 15: The fertile period.** Pregnancy is only possible during ovulation. The **sperm can survive for three days** in the female and the **eggs can survive for one day** after ovulation. Because of this, the woman is fertile for approximately five days.
- **Days 15 to 28:** If pregnancy occurs, the embryo attaches itself to the wall of the womb. If no pregnancy occurs, the lining is not needed and starts to break down again.

The menstrual cycle begins during **puberty** (nine to 14 years of age) and continues until the **menopause**, or 'change of life' (45 to 55 years).

Contraception

- **Rhythm method**: When the egg is released from the ovary, the woman's body temperature rises by about 1°C. If the woman **avoids intercourse** at this time, fertilisation will not take place. This method involves constant measurement of body temperature and can lead to error.

> **key point**
>
> **Contraception** is a practice or device that prevents the fertilisation of an egg by a sperm.

- **The contraceptive pill:** The Pill is a dose of hormones that fools the woman's body into believing fertilisation has taken place. As a result, no egg is released. Overuse can cause health problems in some women.

- **The morning-after pill:** Prevents implantation.

- **The coil:** A device that is attached to the uterus which prevents implantation.

- **Condom:** A rubber sheath that is placed over the penis before intercourse and catches the semen during ejaculation.

- **Sterilisation**: Males are sterilised by having their sperm ducts cut and tied. Females are sterilised by having their fallopian tubes cut and tied. Sterilisation is usually irreversible.

Sample questions and answers

1. *Draw a labelled diagram of the female reproductive system.*

Answer

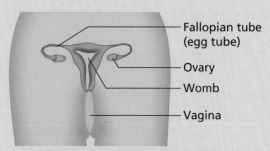

Female reproductive organs

Labels: Fallopian tube (egg tube), Ovary, Womb, Vagina

2. *Where in the body do the following processes occur: (i) sexual intercourse (ii) insemination (iii) fertilisation?*

Answer

(i) Sexual intercourse occurs when the man inserts his penis into the vagina.

(ii) Insemination is the release of sperm into the vagina.

(iii) Fertilisation occurs in the fallopian tube.

3. *What is menstruation?*

Answer

The lining of the womb breaks down for the first five days or so of the woman's cycle and is ejected through her vagina.

4. *What is the function of the placenta?*

Answer

The placenta is a filter that allows food and water to pass from the mother to the embryo and carbon dioxide and other wastes to pass from the embryo to the mother.

9 Genetics

Genetics is the study of heredity.

Inherited characteristics are determined by our **genes** – they are passed on from our parents. Examples include hair colour, shape of face, height, etc.

Non-inherited characteristics are not inherited from birth – they are learned during life. Examples include how to ride a bicycle, an accent, an interest in sport, etc.

Human cells contain **23 pairs of chromosomes**, except for the male gamete (sperm) and the female gamete (egg), each of which have **23 chromosomes**. When the sperm and egg fuse together, they form a zygote, which has the normal 23 pairs of chromosomes.

Genes are short sections of the chemical DNA, which can reproduce protein. They pass on characteristics from parents to children.

Chromosomes are thread-like structures found in the nucleus of a cell. They are made of protein and DNA (deoxyribonucleic acid).

Genes are short sections of the chemical DNA that can reproduce protein. They pass on characteristics from parents to children.

Chromosomes are thread-like structures found in the nucleus of a cell. They are made of protein and DNA (deoxyribonucleic acid).

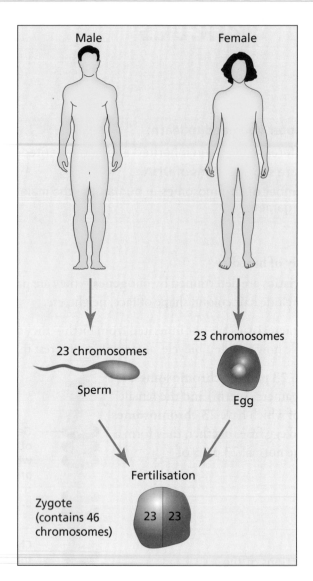

Sample questions and answers

1. *What are (i) genes and (ii) chromosomes?*

Answer

(i) Genes are short sections of the chemical DNA that can reproduce protein. They pass on characteristics from parents to children.

(ii) Chromosomes are thread-like structures found in the nucleus of a cell. They are made of protein and DNA (deoxyribonucleic acid).

2. *What are inherited characteristics?*

Answer

Inherited characteristics are decided from our genes – they are passed on from our parents, such as hair colour, shape of face, height, etc.

10 Plant Structure and Transport in Plants

In this chapter you need to learn:

1. The importance of plants.
2. The structure of plants.
3. The movement of food and water in plants.
4. The factors affecting transpiration.
5. Experiments on the movement of water in plants:
   (a) Absorption of water by roots.
   (b) Water evaporates from the surface of a leaf by transpiration.
   (c) To show water movement through the stem of a plant.

Importance of plants

- A source of oxygen.
- The start of all food chains.
- Can be a source of food.
- A source of materials such as timber, cotton, linen and paper.
- A source of medicines.
- Leisure and aesthetic values.

Plant structure

The main parts of a plant are the root, the stem, the leaf, the flower and the fruit.

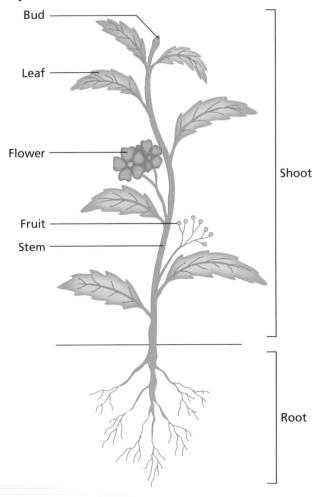

Leaf:

- Makes food by photosynthesis.
- Allows carbon dioxide to move in and oxygen to move out of the plant.
- Releases water from the plant.
- Can be a food store, e.g. lettuce and cabbage.

Stem:

- Carries water and minerals up from the roots to the leaves.
- Carries food down from the leaves to the rest of the plant.
- Can be a food store, e.g. celery and rhubarb.

Roots:

- Absorb water and minerals from the soil.
- Anchor the plant to the ground.
- Can be a food store, e.g. carrot and turnip.

Transport of water and food in plants

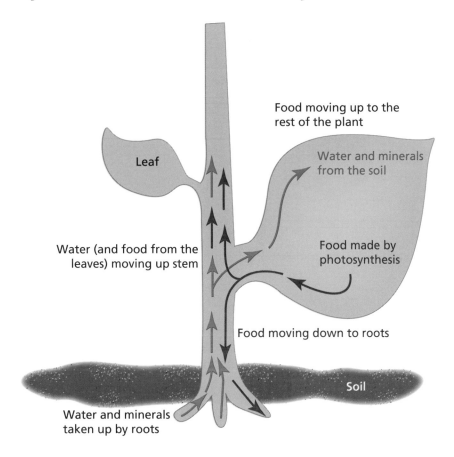

Food moving up to the rest of the plant

Leaf

Water and minerals from the soil

Water (and food from the leaves) moving up stem

Food made by photosynthesis

Food moving down to roots

Soil

Water and minerals taken up by roots

Water and minerals flow up from the roots to the rest of the plant.

Food made in the leaves is carried to other parts of the plant.

- The flow of water from the roots to the leaves is called the **transpiration stream**.
- **Water is lost** through tiny holes called **stomata** in the underside of the leaf.

Transpiration is the loss of water from the leaves of the plant.

The **factors that affect transpiration** are wind, sunlight, humidity, temperature and the amount of water in the soil.

HL

- **Phloem cells** carry **food** from the leaves to the rest of the plant.
- **Xylem cells** carry water and minerals **up** from the roots.

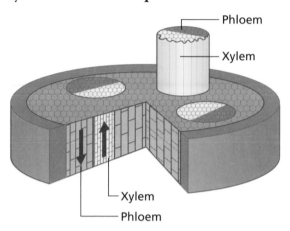

The **transport of food** is affected by temperature and by the amount of oxygen present.

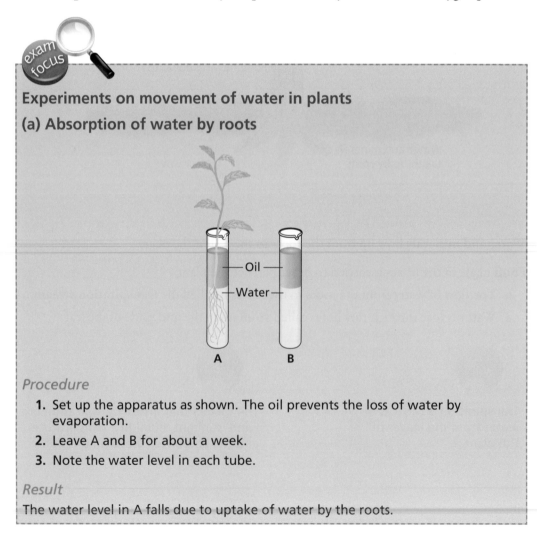

exam focus

Experiments on movement of water in plants

(a) Absorption of water by roots

Procedure

1. Set up the apparatus as shown. The oil prevents the loss of water by evaporation.
2. Leave A and B for about a week.
3. Note the water level in each tube.

Result

The water level in A falls due to uptake of water by the roots.

(b) Water evaporates from the surface of a leaf by transpiration

Procedure

1. Place a growing plant in soil.
2. Seal off the roots by tying a polythene bag around the stem.
3. Leave the plant in a warm place for several hours.

Result

There are droplets of water on the inside of the polythene bag. Test the water with cobalt chloride paper. The cobalt chloride turns from blue to pink.

The use of cobalt chloride paper to test for water is being discontinued on health and safety grounds. It will still be used in examination questions. Anhydrous copper sulphate should be used instead to test for water. When water drops fall on anhydrous copper sulphate it turns blue.

(c) To show water movement through the stem of a plant

Celery

Coloured
water

Procedure

1. Place some food colouring in a beaker of water.
2. Stand the celery stem in the water and leave for two or three days.
3. Take the celery out of the water and examine the veins.
4. Cut across the stem and leaf in sections.

Result

Coloured water is present in the stem and leaves. It has travelled up the stem and into the leaves.

Sample questions and answers

1. *Name two processes that (i) the leaf (ii) the stem and (iii) the root of a green plant carry out.*

Answer

(i) The leaf makes food by photosynthesis, allows carbon dioxide to move in and oxygen to move out of the plant, releases water from the plant and can be a food store.

(ii) The stem carries water and minerals up from the roots to the leaves, carries food down from the leaves to the rest of the plant and can be a food store.

(iii) The roots absorb water and minerals from the soil, anchor the plant to the ground and can be a food store.

2. *Water evaporates from cells in the leaves of plants by way of tiny pores in their leaves. (Junior Cert 2006, Q1c)*

(a) *What is this process called?*

Answer

Transpiration.

(b) *What are the tiny pores called?*

Answer

Stomata.

(c) *How would you test that the liquid which evaporates is water?*

Answer

Test with cobalt chloride paper. The cobalt chloride turns from blue to pink.

11 # Photosynthesis and Tropisms

aims **In this chapter you need to learn:**

1. Green plants make food by photosynthesis.
2. How photosynthesis works.
3. The word equation for photosynthesis.
4. Mandatory experiment: To show that starch is made by a photosynthesising plant.
5. Plants respond to stimuli called tropisms.
6. Phototropism and geotropism.

How photosynthesis works

Plants make **glucose** from carbon dioxide and water by using the energy from the sun and a catalyst called chlorophyll. Glucose can be used as energy, stored as starch, converted into protein or used to make cell walls.

Most leaves are broad, flat and thin. This allows the maximum amount of light to be absorbed and also allows carbon dioxide in quickly.

Green plants make food by **photosynthesis**.

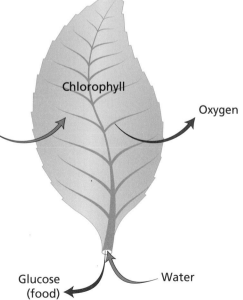

Sun

Energy

Chlorophyll

Oxygen

Carbon dioxide

Glucose (food)

Water

- **Carbon dioxide** is taken in through tiny holes in the leaf called stomata.
- **Water** is taken up from the roots.
- **Energy** is provided by the sun.
- **Chlorophyll** acts as a catalyst.
- **Oxygen** is released through the stomata.
- **Glucose** is transported to the rest of the plant.

The word equation for photosynthesis is

carbon dioxide + water + sunlight + chlorophyll $\rightarrow$ glucose + oxygen

exam focus

Mandatory experiment

To show that starch is produced by a photosynthesising plant

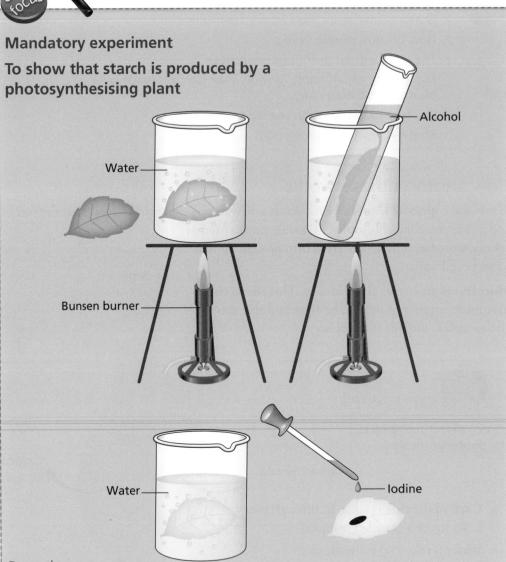

Water

Bunsen burner

Alcohol

Water

Iodine

Procedure

1. Boil the leaf in water to kill the leaf and break open the cells.
2. Boil the leaf in alcohol to remove the chlorophyll.
3. Rinse with water to soften the leaf.
4. Add iodine to the leaf.

Result

If starch is present, the leaf turns black. A yellow-brown colour indicates no starch.

Responsiveness in plants

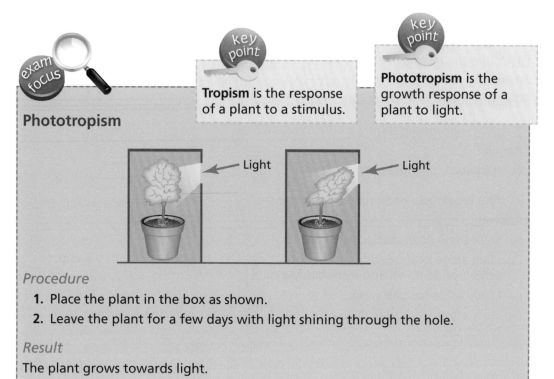

exam focus

Phototropism

> **key point**
> **Tropism** is the response of a plant to a stimulus.

> **key point**
> **Phototropism** is the growth response of a plant to light.

← Light   ← Light

Procedure

1. Place the plant in the box as shown.
2. Leave the plant for a few days with light shining through the hole.

Result

The plant grows towards light.

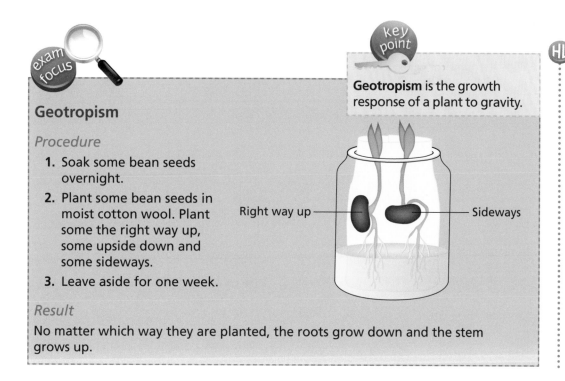

exam focus

Geotropism

> **key point**
> **Geotropism** is the growth response of a plant to gravity.

HL

Procedure

1. Soak some bean seeds overnight.
2. Plant some bean seeds in moist cotton wool. Plant some the right way up, some upside down and some sideways.
3. Leave aside for one week.

Right way up —   — Sideways

Result

No matter which way they are planted, the roots grow down and the stem grows up.

Sample questions and answers

1. *Name the factors necessary for photosynthesis.*

Answer

Carbon dioxide, water, sunlight and chlorophyll.

2. *What is produced during photosynthesis?*

Answer

Food (glucose or starch) and oxygen.

3. *How would you demonstrate geotropism?*

Answer

(i)   Soak some bean seeds overnight.

(ii) Plant some bean seeds in moist cotton wool. Plant some the right way up, some upside down and some sideways.

(iii) Leave aside for one week.

(iv) No matter which way they are planted, the roots grow down and the stem grows up.

12 Plant Reproduction

In this chapter you need to learn:

1. Asexual reproduction involves only one parent.
2. Sexual reproduction occurs when a male gamete (sex cell) fuses with a female gamete (sex cell).
3. The structure of a flower.
4. Pollination and methods of pollination.
5. Fertilisation occurs after pollination.
6. Seed structure and methods of seed dispersal.
7. Germination is the growth of a seed into a new plant.
8. Mandatory experiment: To investigate the conditions necessary for germination.

Asexual reproduction

All offspring are identical to the parent. Examples include mushroom spores, daffodil bulbs, crocus corms, potato tubers, iris rhizomes, strawberry runners and all cuttings and graftings.

key point

Asexual reproduction involves only one parent. No fusion of gametes (sex cells) is involved.

key point

Sexual reproduction occurs when a male gamete (sex cell) fuses with a female gamete (sex cell).

Structure of a flower

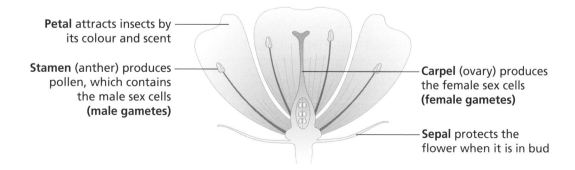

Petal attracts insects by its colour and scent

Stamen (anther) produces pollen, which contains the male sex cells **(male gametes)**

Carpel (ovary) produces the female sex cells **(female gametes)**

Sepal protects the flower when it is in bud

HL

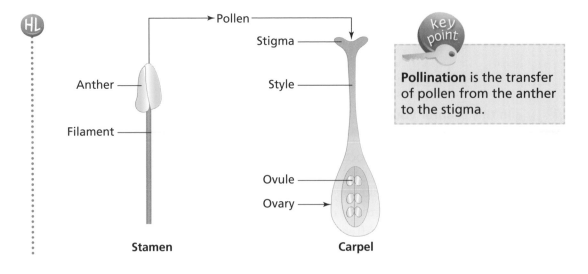

Stamen   **Carpel**

Pollination is the transfer of pollen from the anther to the stigma.

Methods of pollination

- **Insects:** Bees and other insects carry pollen from one flower to another.
- **Wind:** The wind blows pollen from one flower to another.

Differences between insect- and wind-pollinated flowers

Part of flower	Insect pollinated	Wind pollinated
Petals	Large, coloured, scented	Small, green, often unscented
Stamens	Inside flower	Hang outside flower
Pollen grains	Large	Small
Stigma	Small, inside flower	Feathery, hangs outside

Fertilisation

1. A pollen grain falls on the stigma.
2. A tube grows from the pollen grain down into the stigma towards the female ovary.

Fertilisation occurs when the male gamete fuses with the female gamete to form a zygote.

3. The male sex cell moves down the tube and enters the female sex cell.
4. The male sex cell fuses with the female sex cell. The fertilised ovule becomes a **seed**.
5. The ovary swells up and becomes a fruit.

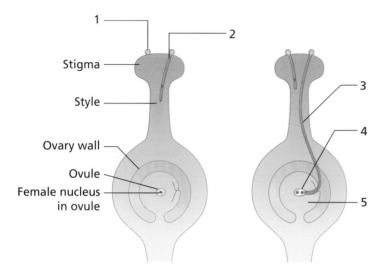

Seeds

Seeds have a hard outer coating called a **testa**. This contains a **food supply** that allows the seed to develop into a new plant.

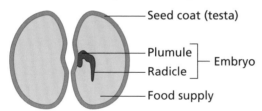

Seed structure

A seed is a food store that is contained inside a hard case called a testa. When the seed begins to germinate, a young root (**radicle**) emerges and then a young shoot (**plumule**) emerges.

Methods of seed dispersal

- **Wind:** Dandelions and thistles have 'parachutes' that float in the wind.
- **Animal:** Burdock seeds stick to animals and are carried away. Berries are eaten by animals and are passed out later.
- **Self-dispersal:** Peas burst out of their pods.
- **Water:** Water lilies produce seeds that can float away.

Seed germination

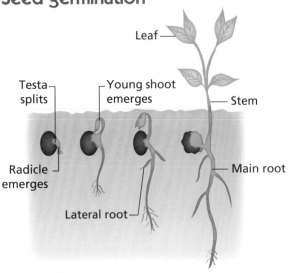

Germination is the growth of the seed into a new plant.

Mandatory experiment

To investigate the conditions necessary for germination

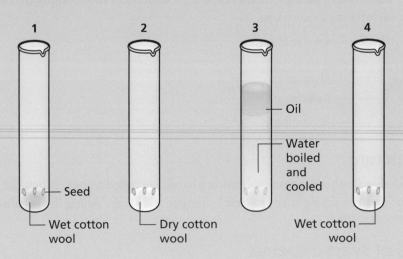

Procedure
1. Set up four test tubes as shown in the diagram.
2. Place test tubes 1, 2 and 3 in a warm spot (20°C) and leave test tube 4 in a fridge (4°C).
3. Leave them for a few days. Do not allow the cotton wool in test tubes 1 and 4 to dry out.

Result
The seeds in test tube 1 germinated.

Conclusion

Air, water and heat are conditions necessary for germination.

Diagram 1	Diagram 2	Diagram 3	Diagram 4
20°C	20°C	20°C'	4°C
Wet cotton wool	Dry cotton wool	Water boiled and cooled	Wet cotton wool
Germinates	Does not germinate	Does not germinate	Does not germinate
Has air, water and heat	Has no water	Has no air	Has no heat

Sample questions and answers

1. *Draw a labelled diagram of the structure of a flower. Describe the function of each part.*

   Answer

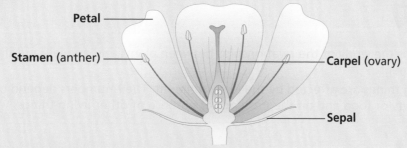

   Petal — Stamen (anther) — Carpel (ovary) — Sepal

   The sepal protects the flower when it is in bud.
   The petal attracts insects by its colour and scent.
   The carpel produces the female sex cells.
   The stamen produces pollen, which contains the male sex cells.

2. **(a)** *What is fertilisation?*

   Answer

   Fertilisation is when the male gamete fuses with (joins) the female gamete to produce a zygote.

   (b) *When does fertilisation in a plant occur?*

   Answer

   After pollination.

   (c) *Describe the main methods of seed dispersal.*

   Answer

   (i) Wind: Dandelions and thistles have 'parachutes' that float in the wind.
   (ii) Animal: Burdock seeds stick to animals and are carried away. Berries are eaten by animals and are passed out later.
   (iii) Self-dispersal: Peas burst out of their pods.
   (iv) Water: Water lilies produce seeds that can float away.

13 Ecology and Habitat Study

 In this chapter you need to learn:

1. The definitions and examples of ecology, habitats and ecosystems.
2. Examples and definitions of feeding relationships: transfer of energy, producers and consumers, carnivores, herbivores, omnivores and decomposers, food chains and food webs, pyramid of numbers, adaptation, competition and interdependence.
3. Human effects on the environment: balance of nature, deforestation, conservation, waste management and pollution, greenhouse effect and the ozone layer.
4. Mandatory experiment: To study a local habitat, using appropriate instruments and simple keys.

Ecology is the study of the relationships between plants and animals and their environment.

All living things are affected by their environment. Their numbers depend on the availability of food and on the presence or absence of other living things.

A **habitat** is the place where an organism lives. Examples of habitats include woodland, seashore, a pond and many others.

An **ecosystem** is the combination of the animal and plant community with their environment.

Feeding relationships

Transfer of energy: Energy is transferred from the sun to plants. The plants produce food by photosynthesis. Plants transfer this food energy to animals.

Producers are plants that make food by photosynthesis.

Consumers are organisms that cannot make food. Consumers include animals, fungi and most bacteria.

- **Herbivores** are animals that eat plants, e.g. cows and sheep.
- **Carnivores** are animals that eat other animals, e.g. foxes.
- **Omnivores** are animals that eat both plants and animals, e.g. humans.

Decomposers are organisms that break down dead animal and plant matter, e.g. bacteria and fungi.

- A **food chain** is a sequence of organisms in which each organism provides food for the next organism.
- A **food web** is a number of interconnecting food chains.

Food chains and food webs

Plants form the first link in a food chain.

grass ⟹ rabbit ⟹ fox
pond weed ⟹ tadpole ⟹ beetle ⟹ pike

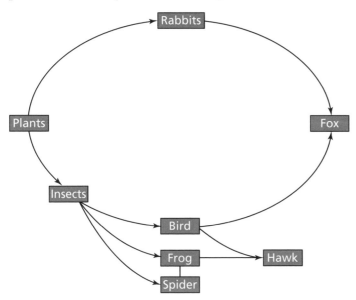

Adaptations are special features or habits that animals and plants have which enable them to survive in their environment. For example, squirrels have sharp teeth for eating nuts, large eyes on the side of their head to enable them to see over a wide viewing range and many other special features. Flowers have attractive colours and scent, which attract insects for pollination.

Pyramid of numbers

A **primary consumer** needs many small plants to feed on. A **secondary consumer** is usually a larger animal than a primary consumer and needs more food to feed on.

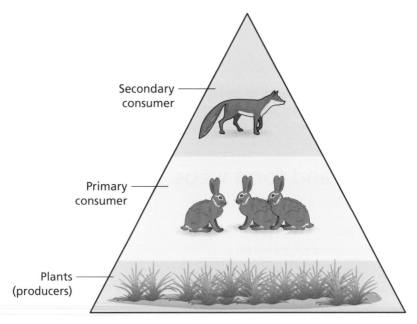

Secondary consumer

Primary consumer

Plants (producers)

Competition: Animals and plants compete with each other for many things, such as light, food, water, territory, shelter and partners.

Interdependence: Animals and plants depend on each other for survival.

- Plants depend on animals for pollination and for seed dispersal.
- Dead animals and their waste products provide fertile soil for plants.
- Animals produce carbon dioxide, which is necessary for photosynthesis.
- Plants produce oxygen during photosynthesis, which helps animals to breathe.

Balance of nature

The feeding relationships in an ecosystem are a fine balance. Too many or too little of one species can alter the number of another species. For example, too many foxes in a habitat would mean fewer rabbits. If the number of foxes was reduced, the population of rabbits would increase. The larger rabbit population would then eat more plants, upsetting the balance of nature.

Human effects on the environment

Deforestation and desertification

Deforestation is the removal of large areas of trees. Removal of trees leads to a loss of oxygen, increases the amount of carbon dioxide and can also cause erosion or desertification. **Desertification** is the cutting down of large forest areas, resulting in large areas of dry, dusty soil.

Conservation

Conservation is the management of our natural resources through protection and preservation.

Waste management

Human activity, agriculture, fisheries and industry all produce vast amounts of waste. It is essential that this waste be managed. The main ways are:

- **Reducing** the amount of unnecessary goods, e.g. plastic bags.
- **Reusing** materials, e.g. glass bottles.
- **Recycling** as much as possible, e.g. glass, paper, aluminium, food and garden waste.
- **Disposal** of waste using legal means of incineration and landfill.

Pollution

- **Water pollution** is the introduction of anything into water that alters any of its beneficial uses, e.g. sailing, fishing, drinking.
- **Atmospheric pollution** is the introduction of small, suspended solids or poisonous liquids and gases into the air.
- **Acid rain** is caused by an increase in the pH of normal rainwater by the introduction of sulphur dioxide and the oxides of nitrogen into the air.
- **Greenhouse effect:** Certain gases in the air absorb UV radiation, which causes an increase in the temperature of the earth. Carbon dioxide, methane and CFCs are some examples of greenhouse gases.

Pollution is any undesirable change in our environment caused by human activities.

Ozone layer

A layer of ozone gas protects us from the harmful effects of radiation from the sun. Some gases, particularly CFCs, have created a hole in the ozone layer.

Effects of human activity on the environment

Positive effects	Negative effects
Treatment of waste – sewage	Burning fossil fuels – greenhouse effect
Recycling plastic, glass and aluminium cans	Use of CFCs, which damage the ozone layer
Restocking fish in rivers	Fish kills caused by silage and slurry
Government levies, e.g. on plastic bags	Discharge of nitrates and phosphates into water

Mandatory experiment

To study a local habitat, using appropriate instruments and simple keys

Woodland Visit

27 April 2012

Investigation by G. Hughes

Introduction

The woodland was visited to show the variety and distribution of named organisms.

Procedure

(a) **Variety of organisms**

1. The class group visited the woodland in Glen of the Downs outside Dublin.
2. The class brought pooters, quadrats, nets, beating trays and pitfall traps with us.
3. The class looked at leaves, at the soil, under stones, in cracks in the ground and in cracks in trees.
4. The class captured some animals with the pooters, nets and pitfall traps.
5. The class recorded the results in the form of a table.

Results

Plants	Animals	
	Vertebrates	Invertebrates
Grass	Red squirrel	Wood louse
Moss	Grey squirrel	Millipede
Wild garlic	Robin	Butterfly
Wild woodbine	Wren	Spider
Oak	Mouse	
Birch		
Beech		

(b) Distribution of plants

1. The class used a quadrat to find the average distribution of plants in an area of the woodland.
2. The quadrat was thrown at random. The type of plants found inside the quadrat was recorded.
3. The quadrat was thrown ten times in total.
4. A table was used to record the results. The percentage frequency of each plant was then calculated.

Plant	Quadrat number										Total	Frequency
	1	2	3	4	5	6	7	8	9	10		
Wild garlic	X		X	X		X		X		X	6	60%
Moss		X			X		X				3	30%
Fern		X		X							2	20%
Satin flower	X		X		X		X		X		5	50%

(c) Using a simple key

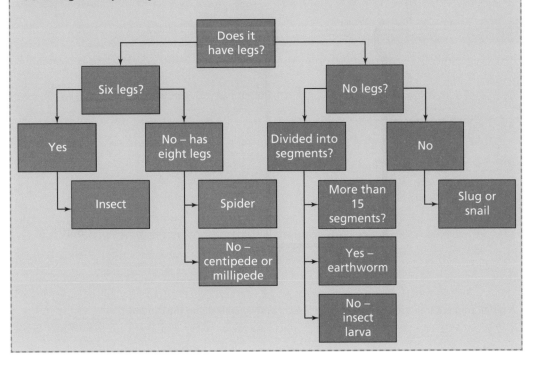

Using a pooter

Suck

A **pooter** is an instrument used to collect small insects by sucking them up.

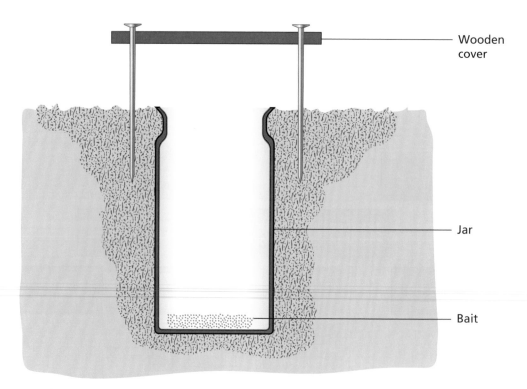

Wooden cover

Jar

Bait

A **pitfall trap** is a trap used to collect small insects as they walk along the ground.

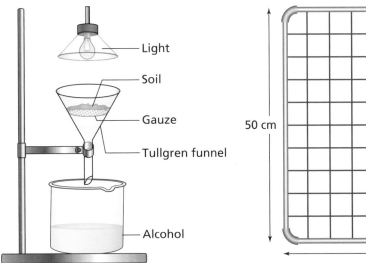

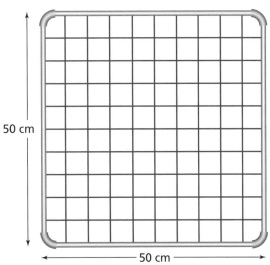

A **Tullgren funnel** is used to collect small animals and micro-organisms from soil or leaf litter.

A **quadrat** is a square frame that is thrown a number of times at random in a habitat. It is used to estimate the number of plants in a habitat.

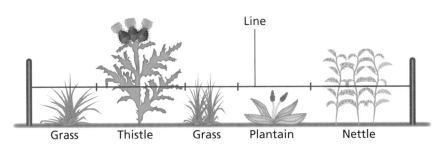

A **line transect** is a piece of twine or rope marked at regular intervals which is stretched across a habitat to estimate the number of plants present. It is used to study plant variations from one part of a habitat to another. A piece of twine or rope is stretched across a habitat. The name and height of each plant touching the rope at regular intervals (1 m) is recorded.

Sample questions and answers

1. *How is random sampling achieved when using a quadrat? (Junior Cert 2009, Q3)*

Answer

A quadrat is a square frame that is thrown a number of times at random in a habitat. It is used to estimate the number of plants in a habitat.

2. *Give two different types of data collected at each site in the habitat.*

Answer

(i) The total number of plants collected.

(ii) The average distribution.

3. *What is a line transect?*

Answer

A line transect is a piece of twine or rope marked at regular intervals that is stretched across a habitat to estimate the number of plants present.

4. *Describe how to sample a habitat using a line transect.*

Answer

A piece of twine or rope is stretched across a habitat. The name and height of each plant touching the rope at regular intervals (1 m) is recorded.

5. *A sweep net is often used to collect small animals. Draw a labelled diagram of another instrument that can be used to collect small animals.*

Answer

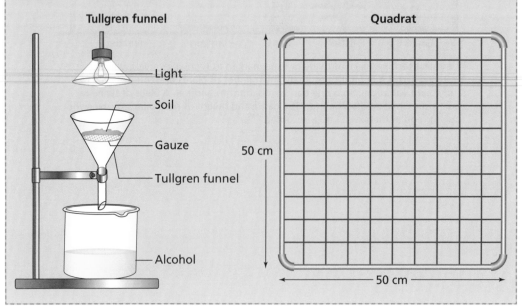

Tullgren funnel

Light

Soil

Gauze

Tullgren funnel

Alcohol

50 cm

Quadrat

50 cm

14 Micro-organisms

In this chapter you need to learn:

1. Some micro-organisms are beneficial, while others are harmful.
2. Viruses, bacteria and some fungi are micro-organisms.
3. Uses of biotechnology.
4. Mandatory experiment: To investigate the presence of micro-organisms in air and soil.

Micro-organisms

Micro-organisms are very small organisms. Some micro-organisms are beneficial to humans; others are harmful.

Viruses are micro-organisms that multiply only in living cells by making replicas of themselves. Viruses cause influenza, colds, polio, AIDS and many more illnesses.

Bacteria are single cells that can reproduce very quickly.

Harmful bacteria cause diseases such as pneumonia, tuberculosis and salmonella.

Fungi have no chlorophyll and cannot produce food by photosynthesis. Many fungi, such as mushrooms, are not micro-organisms.

Biotechnology

Biotechnology is the use of animals, plants and micro-organisms to produce useful products.

Uses of biotechnology

In industry	In medicine
Yeast to make alcohol and bread	Bacteria and fungi are used to make antibiotics
Bacteria are used to make enzymes for washing powders	Bacteria and yeast are used to make hormones, clotting agents and antibodies

Mandatory experiment

To investigate the presence of micro-organisms in air and in soil

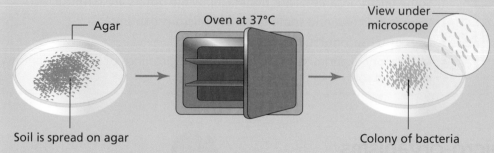

Agar — Oven at 37°C — View under microscope

Soil is spread on agar — Colony of bacteria

Procedure

1. Prepare three sterile Petri dishes containing nutrient agar.
2. Seal one dish. (This acts as a control to compare with the other two dishes.)
3. Leave the second dish exposed to the air for some minutes. Seal it.
4. Use a sterile rod to place some soil on the third dish.
5. Incubate the three dishes at 37°C for 72 hours.

Result

Shiny patches of bacteria and fungi will appear as colonies on the dishes that were exposed to the air and which contained the soil.

Conclusion

Air and soil contain micro-organisms.

Sample question and answer

1. *Describe an experiment to investigate the presence of micro-organisms in soil.*

Answer

(i)   Prepare three sterile Petri dishes containing nutrient agar.

(ii) Seal one dish. (This acts as a control to compare with the other two dishes.)

(iii) Leave the second dish exposed to the air for some minutes. Seal it.

(iv) Use a sterile rod to place some soil on the third dish.

(v) Incubate the three dishes at 37°C for 72 hours.

(vi) Shiny patches of bacteria and fungi will appear as colonies on the dishes that were exposed to the air and which contained the soil.

CHEMISTRY

15 **Elements, Compounds and Mixtures**

What is chemistry?

Chemistry is the study of substances and how they can be broken up and changed.

- Matter occupies space.
- Matter has mass.
- All matter is made up of **particles**. Elements, compounds and mixtures are all made up of particles.
- Matter can exist in three forms or states. The three states of matter are solids, liquids and gases.
- Matter can be interchanged.

  solid ⟺ **liquid** ⟺ **gas**
  ice   ⟺ water   ⟺ steam

key point

All substances are made up of **matter**.

Characteristics of matter

Property	Solid	Liquid	Gas
Attractive forces	Strong	Weak	Very weak
Shape	Definite	Not definite; depends on container	Not definite; fills any container
Volume	Definite	Definite	Not definite
Mobility	Fixed but can vibrate	Ability to flow	Completely free movement

All matter is made from particles.

- Movement of particles was first noticed by Robert Brown, who saw pollen grains zigzagging around in water. This movement is called **Brownian movement**.

- Solids, liquids and gases are all made from particles. Whether a substance is a solid, a liquid or a gas depends on how freely and how fast the particles move.

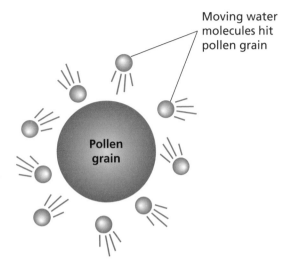

Moving water molecules hit pollen grain

Pollen grain

Elements and atoms

All substances are made up of tiny particles called atoms. When a substance is made up of only one type of atom, it is called an element. The element iron is made up of iron atoms, the element hydrogen is made up of hydrogen atoms, the element sulphur is made up of sulphur atoms and so on.

An **atom** is the smallest particle of an element that still retains the properties of that element.

An **element** is a substance that cannot be broken down into simpler substances by chemical reactions.

Compounds and elements

When elements combine together by means of a chemical reaction, they form new substances called compounds. For example, when the elements hydrogen and oxygen combine together they form the compound water (H_2O).

The compound water is a colourless liquid. The elements used to make water have different physical and chemical properties. Hydrogen and oxygen are colourless gases and are highly reactive.

A **compound** is formed when two or more elements combine chemically.

Properties of elements and compounds

Elements	Compounds
Hydrogen (H$_2$): A colourless, odourless, tasteless gas. Explosive when mixed with oxygen. **Oxygen (O$_2$):** A colourless, odourless, tasteless gas. Substances need oxygen to burn.	**Water (H$_2$O):** A colourless liquid, nice taste, essential for life. It does not burn. Excellent solvent.
Carbon (C): A black solid. **Oxygen (O$_2$):** A colourless, odourless, tasteless gas. Substances need oxygen to burn.	**Carbon dioxide (CO$_2$):** A colourless, odourless, tasteless gas. Does not allow substances to burn.
Magnesium (Mg): A silver metal solid. **Oxygen (O$_2$):** A colourless, odourless, tasteless gas. Substances need oxygen to burn.	**Magnesium oxide (MgO):** A solid white powder.
Iron (Fe): A dark grey metal. It is attracted to magnets. **Sulphur (S):** A yellow solid.	**Iron sulphide (FeS):** A black solid. It is not attracted to magnets.

Molecules and compounds

- Hydrogen (H$_2$) and oxygen (O$_2$) are not compounds. They are molecules made of a single element.
- Carbon dioxide (CO$_2$) and methane (CH$_4$) are compounds. They are made from more than one element.
- Sodium chloride (NaCl) and magnesium oxide (MgO) are compounds. The elements are joined together in giant structures called **lattices** and are not molecules.

A **molecule** is two or more atoms chemically combined together. It is the smallest particle of an element or a compound that can exist on its own.

Compounds and mixtures

Not all substances are made up of elements combined together chemically. Many are just mixed or jumbled up together. Substances like air, seawater and crude oil are mixtures.

Mixtures of metals are called **alloys.**

A **mixture** is formed when two or more substances are put together but are not chemically combined.

Magnet can separate iron from mixture before heating

Magnet cannot separate iron from substance after heating

When sulphur and iron filings are mixed together, they form a mixture.
When sulphur and iron filings are **heated** together, they form a compound (iron sulphide).

Differences between mixtures and compounds

Mixture	Compound
Consists of two or more substances	Consists of a single substance
The amounts of the substances can vary	The amounts of the elements in a compound are fixed
Can often be easily separated	Can only be separated into its elements by chemical reaction
Properties are similar to the substances used to make the mixture	Properties are very different to the elements that made the compound

Sample questions and answers

1. *Iron and sulphur are **elements**. When iron and sulphur are heated, they form a* **compound**.

   (a) *What is an element?*

   Answer

   An element is a substance that cannot be broken down into simpler substances by chemical reactions.

   (b) *Give a simple test to show that a compound and not a mixture are formed when iron and sulphur are heated.*

   Answer

   A magnet can separate the iron from the mixture before heating. A magnet cannot separate the iron from the compound formed after heating.

16 The Periodic Table, Metals, Alkali and Alkaline Earth Metals

The **periodic table** is an arrangement of elements in order of increasing atomic mass.

There are **92 elements** that occur in nature. Scientists have made another 12 artificially. The elements are arranged in an orderly manner, like goods in a supermarket.

In a supermarket, similar items are arranged into groups – apples are on one shelf, oranges are on another, breakfast cereals are on another and so on. Like the items on the supermarket shelves, elements can also be arranged into groups.

	Group 1	Group 2												Group 3	Group 4	Group 5	Group 6	Group 7	Group 0
1st Period	1 **H** hydrogen 1																		4 **He** helium 2
2nd Period	7 **Li** lithium 3	9 **Be** beryllium 4												11 **B** boron 5	12 **C** carbon 6	14 **N** nitrogen 7	16 **O** oxygen 8	19 **F** fluorine 9	20 **Ne** neon 10
3rd Period	23 **Na** sodium 11	24 **Mg** magnesium 12												27 **Al** aluminium 13	28 **Si** silicon 14	31 **P** phosphorus 15	32 **S** sulphur 16	35.5 **Cl** chlorine 17	40 **Ar** argon 18
4th Period	39 **K** potassium 19	40 **Ca** calcium 20	45 **Sc** scandium 21	48 **Ti** titanium 22	51 **V** vanadium 23	52 **Cr** chromium 24	55 **Mn** manganese 25	56 **Fe** iron 26	59 **Co** cobalt 27	59 **Ni** nickel 28	64 **Cu** copper 29	65 **Zn** zinc 30		70 **Ga** gallium 31	73 **Ge** germanium 32	75 **As** arsenic 33	79 **Se** selenium 34	80 **Br** bromine 35	84 **Kr** krypton 36
5th Period	85.5 **Rb** rubidium 37	88 **Sr** strontium 38	89 **Y** yttrium 39	91 **Zr** zirconium 40	93 **Nb** niobium 41	96 **Mo** molybdenum 42	99 **Tc** technetium 43	101 **Ru** ruthenium 44	103 **Rh** rhodium 45	106 **Pd** palladium 46	108 **Ag** silver 47	112 **Cd** cadmium 48		115 **In** indium 49	119 **Sn** tin 50	122 **Sb** antimony 51	127 **Te** tellurium 52	128 **I** iodine 53	131 **Xe** xenon 54
6th Period	133 **Cs** caesium 55	137 **Ba** barium 56	139 **La** lanthanum 57	178 **Hf** hafnium 72	181 **Ta** tantalum 73	184 **W** tungsten 74	186 **Re** rhenium 75	190 **Os** osmium 76	192 **Ir** iridium 77	195 **Pt** platinum 78	197 **Au** gold 79	201 **Hg** mercury 80		204 **Tl** thallium 81	207 **Pb** lead 82	209 **Bi** bismuth 83	210 **Po** polonium 84	210 **At** astatine 85	222 **Rn** radon 86
7th Period	223 **Fr** francium 87	226 **Ra** radium 88	227 **Ac** actinium 89																

140 **Ce** cerium 58	141 **Pr** praseodymium 59	144 **Nd** neodymium 60	147 **Pm** promethium 61	150 **Sm** samarium 62	152 **Eu** europium 63	157 **Gd** gadolinium 64	159 **Tb** terbium 65	162.5 **Dy** dysprosium 66	165 **Ho** holmium 67	167 **Er** erbium 68	169 **Tm** thulium 69	173 **Yb** ytterbium 70	175 **Lu** lutetium 71
232 **Th** thorium 90	231 **Pa** protactinium 91	238 **U** uranium 92	237 **Np** neptunium 93	242 **Pu** plutonium 94	243 **Am** americium 95	247 **Cm** curium 96	247 **Bk** berkelium 97	251 **Cf** californium 98	254 **Es** einsteinium 99	253 **Fm** fermium 100	256 **Md** mendelevium 101	254 **No** nobelium 102	257 **Lr** lawrencium 103

The zigzag line separates the metals from the non-metals.

Metal

Non-metal

Elements that have similar physical and chemical properties are arranged into groups.

- Mendeleev arranged the periodic table in this way and also put elements with **similar properties** in the same vertical column.
- Vertical columns are called **groups**. Group 7 contains the similar elements lithium, sodium and potassium.
- Horizontal rows are called **periods**.
- About 80 per cent of the elements are **metals**. These are on the left-hand side of the zigzag line.
- On the right of this line are the **non-metals**.

Metals and non-metals

Elements	Symbol	State	Colour
Metals			
Copper	Cu	Solid	Pink-brown
Zinc	Zn	Solid	Silver-grey
Aluminium	Al	Solid	Silver-grey
Iron	Fe	Solid	Dark grey
Silver	Ag	Solid	Silver
Gold	Au	Solid	Yellow
Non-metals			
Hydrogen	H	Gas	Colourless
Carbon	C	Solid	Black
Oxygen	O	Gas	Colourless
Nitrogen	N	Gas	Colourless
Sulphur	S	Solid	Yellow

Properties of metals

- **Metals are lustrous:** All metals are shiny.
- **Metals are malleable:** Metals can be hammered and shaped.
- **Metals are ductile:** Metals can be stretched.
- **Metals are usually strong, hard solids:** Most metals are hard and strong. Sodium and the other alkali metals are soft.
- **Metals are good conductors of heat and electricity:** Heat energy and electrons can move through metals easily.

Alloy	Mixture of elements	Uses
Steel	Iron, carbon and other elements	Construction, machinery, motor vehicles, etc.
Brass	Copper and zinc	Door handles, musical instruments, etc.
Bronze	Copper and tin	Statues
Solder	Lead and tin	Joining connections together in electrical circuits

Corrosion and rusting

- When metals react with oxygen and water, they corrode. This chemical reaction is an oxidation reaction.
- **Rusting** is iron corrosion. Water and oxygen are necessary for rusting.
- **Corrosion** returns metals to their ore, e.g. iron is changed into iron oxide.
- **Preventing corrosion:** Painting, electroplating, greasing, galvanising, anodising and alloying can all be used to prevent corrosion.

key point

Alloys are mixtures of metals. Some alloys contain the non-metal carbon.

Mandatory experiment

To demonstrate that oxygen and water are necessary for rusting

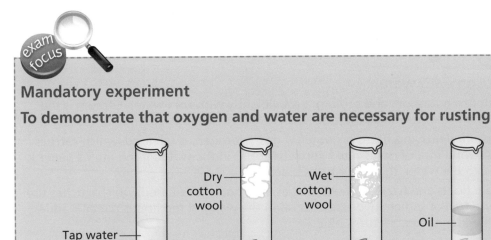

A — Tap water, Clean iron nail
B — Dry cotton wool, Calcium chloride
C — Wet cotton wool
D — Oil, Boiled water

Procedure

1. Set up four test tubes as shown. Place three identical nails in each tube.
2. Leave the test tubes to stand for a few days.
3. Rusting takes place in A and in C. Both contain oxygen and water.

Results

1. Test tubes A and C contain rust.
2. There is more rust in test tube C because it contains more oxygen than A.

Conclusion

Oxygen and water are necessary for rusting.

HL The alkali metals

- The alkali metals are in **Group 1** of the periodic table.
- Lithium, sodium, potassium, rubidium and caesium are called the alkali metals because they react with water to form **alkaline (basic) solutions**.
- They have similar physical and chemical properties because they each have **one electron** in their outer shell.
- They are soft, shiny metals that are stored in oil because they react with air and water.

Reaction with air (oxygen)

The alkali metals react with oxygen to form metal oxides. They lose their shiny appearance when they are exposed to air.

$$\text{lithium} + \text{oxygen} \Rightarrow \text{lithium oxide}$$

$$\text{sodium} + \text{oxygen} \Rightarrow \text{sodium oxide}$$

$$\text{potassium} + \text{oxygen} \Rightarrow \text{potassium oxide}$$

exam focus

Reaction with water

Metals like potassium and sodium react violently with cold water. Lithium is the least reactive of the alkali metals.

Potassium floats and fizzes on water. A gas, hydrogen, is released, which catches fire. A white trail of potassium hydroxide forms in the water. If red litmus paper is added to the water, the paper turns blue.

Sodium floats and fizzes on water. A gas, hydrogen, is released, which catches fire. A white trail of sodium hydroxide forms in the water. If red litmus paper is added to the water, the paper turns blue.

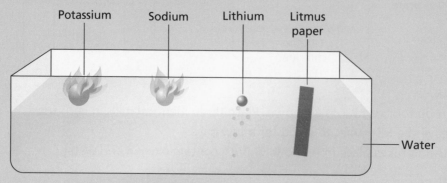

$$\text{potassium} + \text{water} \Rightarrow \text{potassium hydroxide} + \text{hydrogen}$$

$$\text{sodium} + \text{water} \Rightarrow \text{sodium hydroxide} + \text{hydrogen}$$

$$\text{lithium} + \text{water} \Rightarrow \text{lithium hydroxide} + \text{hydrogen}$$

The alkaline earth metals

- The alkaline earth metals are in **Group 2** of the periodic table.
- They are less reactive than the alkali metals.
- The best-known alkaline earth metals are magnesium and calcium.
- Magnesium alloys are used in building aircraft and ships.
- Calcium is the main element in bones, teeth and shells.
- They have similar physical and chemical properties because they each have **two electrons** in their outer shell.

Relative reactivities of some metals (Ca, Mg, Zn and Cu)

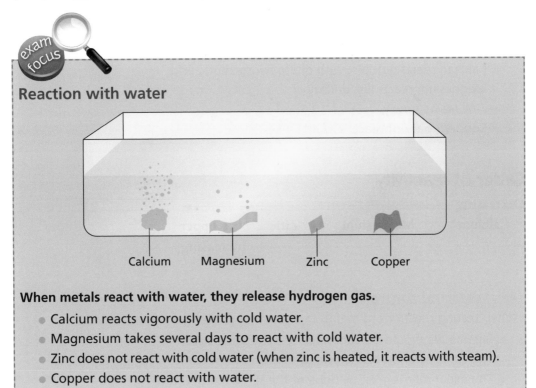

Reaction with water

Calcium   Magnesium   Zinc   Copper

When metals react with water, they release hydrogen gas.

- Calcium reacts vigorously with cold water.
- Magnesium takes several days to react with cold water.
- Zinc does not react with cold water (when zinc is heated, it reacts with steam).
- Copper does not react with water.

Reaction with dilute acids

When metals react with dilute hydrochloric acid, they form salts and release hydrogen gas.

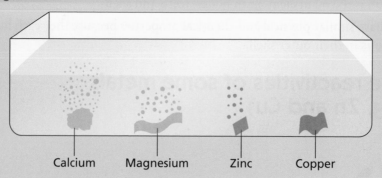

Calcium   Magnesium   Zinc   Copper

- Calcium reacts quickest with dilute hydrochloric acid.
- Magnesium reacts less quickly.
- Zinc reacts slowly.
- Copper does not react.

Order of reactivity

Decreasing ─────────────────────────────→

Calcium   Magnesium   Zinc   Copper

←───────────────────────────── Increasing

Fair tests and controls

When testing reactions of metals in water and dilute hydrochloric acid:

- The metals should be approximately the same size.
- The concentration of the acid used must be the same in each experiment.
- The experiments must be done at the same temperature.

Mandatory experiment

To investigate the reaction between zinc and hydrochloric acid (HCl) and to test for hydrogen

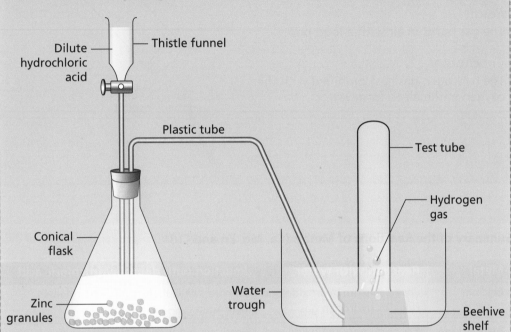

Dilute hydrochloric acid

Thistle funnel

Plastic tube

Test tube

Hydrogen gas

Conical flask

Zinc granules

Water trough

Beehive shelf

Word equation
zinc + hydrochloric acid $\Rightarrow$ zinc chloride + hydrogen

Chemical equation
$Zn + 2HCl \Rightarrow ZnCl_2 + H_2$

Procedure

1. Set up the apparatus as shown in the diagram.
2. Make sure that there are no air bubbles in the test tube and in the plastic delivery tube. Air and hydrogen form an explosive mixture.
3. Add the dilute hydrochloric acid to the zinc granules.
4. Collect the gas produced in the test tube. Collect a further five test tubes of the gas. Put a cork or rubber stopper on each filled test tube.

To test for hydrogen

Procedure

1. Invert a test tube of gas as shown.
2. Remove the stopper.
3. Put a lighted splint in the mouth of the test tube.

Result

The gas burns in air with a loud pop.

Conclusion

The hydrogen gas has combined with the oxygen in the air to form water.

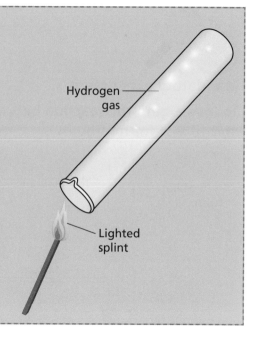

Hydrogen gas

Lighted splint

Summary of the Reactions of Metals (Ca, Mg, Zn and Cu)

Metal	Reaction with water	Reaction with dilute hydrochloric acid
Calcium	Forms calcium hydroxide and releases hydrogen gas	Produces calcium chloride and releases hydrogen gas
Magnesium	Forms magnesium oxide and releases hydrogen gas	Produces magnesium chloride and releases hydrogen gas
Zinc	Forms zinc hydroxide and releases hydrogen gas	Produces zinc chloride and releases hydrogen gas
Copper	No reaction	No reaction

Sample questions and answers

1. *Which group on the periodic table are the alkali metals?*

Answer

Group 1.

2. *What is an alloy?*

Answer

An alloy is a mixture of metals – some alloys also contain the non-metal carbon.

3. *Describe how the metal potassium reacts with water.*

Answer

Potassium reacts violently with water. It floats and fizzes. A gas, hydrogen, is released, which catches fire. A white trail of potassium hydroxide forms in the water. If red litmus paper is added to the water, the paper turns blue.

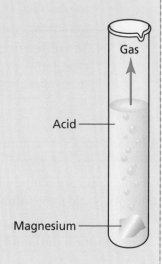

4. *Reactivity tests were carried out on calcium, copper, magnesium and zinc in four test tubes containing an acid. The test carried out using magnesium is shown. (Junior Cert 2006, Q4e)*

State one thing you would do to **make the tests fair**. List the four metals in order of reactivity with the acid, **starting with the most reactive**.

Answer

Fair test:

  (i) Use the same concentration of the same acid each time.

 (ii) Use the same mass of each metal each time.

(iii) Use the same surface area of metal each time.

(iv) Carry out each reaction at the same temperature and pressure.

Most reactive: Calcium, magnesium, zinc, copper.

17 Solutions and Separating Mixtures

 In this chapter you need to learn:

1. A solution is a mixture of a solute and a solvent.
2. The differences between dilute, concentrated and saturated solutions.
3. Mandatory experiment: To investigate the solubility of a variety of substances in water.
4. Mandatory experiment: To investigate the effect of temperature on the solubility of copper sulphate in water.
5. Mandatory experiment: To grow crystals using alum or copper sulphate.
6. The differences between physical and chemical changes.
7. Mandatory experiment: Separation of mixtures by (a) filtration (b) evaporation (c) distillation (d) chromatography.

Solutions are a very common type of mixture. When salt is mixed with water, it dissolves in the water and forms a solution.

When a substance is mixed with a liquid, the substance may dissolve in the liquid. The substance is said to be **soluble** in that liquid and the resulting mixture is called a solution.

- A **solvent** is the liquid in which the solution is made.
- A **solute** is the substance that dissolves in the solvent.
- A **solution** is a mixture of a solute and a solvent.

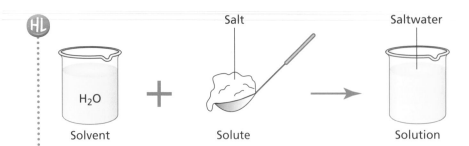

- A **dilute solution** contains **a little solute in a lot of solvent**.
- A **concentrated solution** contains **a lot of solute in a little solvent**.
- A **saturated solution** contains as much solute as can be dissolved at a given temperature.

Mandatory experiment

To investigate the solubility of a variety of substances in water

Procedure

1. Add approximately 100 cm³ of water to a clean beaker.
2. Gradually add some sodium chloride to the water.
3. Stir constantly until no more sodium chloride will dissolve.
4. Repeat steps 1 to 3 using different solutes (sugar, copper sulphate, coffee, alcohol, etc.).

Results

When a solute dissolves in water, it forms a clear solution, i.e. light will pass through it.

Mandatory experiment

To investigate the effect of temperature on the solubility of copper sulphate in water

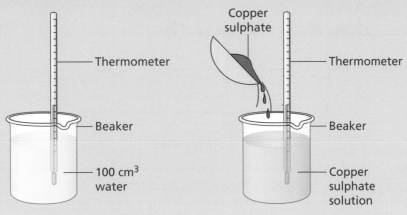

Procedure

1. Use a graduated cylinder to measure 100 cm³ of water into a clean, dry beaker.
2. Find the mass of the beaker and water.
3. Measure the temperature of the water with a thermometer.
4. Gradually add copper sulphate ($CuSO_4$) to the water.

5. Stir constantly until the copper sulphate dissolves.

6. Continue adding the copper sulphate until it will no longer dissolve, but rather settles on the bottom of the beaker.

7. Reweigh the beaker and its contents.

8. Calculate the mass of the copper sulphate that dissolved in the beaker at that temperature.

9. Repeat steps 3 to 8 at different temperatures.

Results

Temperature (°C)	Mass of copper sulphate that dissolved in 100 g of water
0	13
20	17
30	20
40	30
50	35
60	40
70	47
80	56

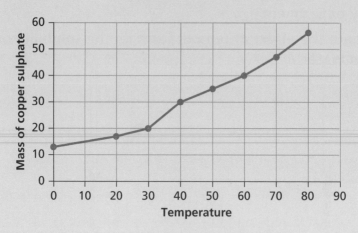

Conclusion

The hotter the water, the more solute will dissolve.

Mandatory experiment

To grow crystals using alum or copper sulphate

Procedure

1. Allow the copper sulphate from the previous investigation to cool.

2. This may be speeded up by placing the beaker in a basin of iced water. Alternatively, the beaker can be set aside and left for a week or so.

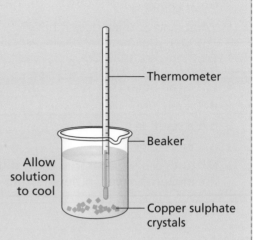

Thermometer

Beaker

Allow solution to cool

Copper sulphate crystals

Results

Crystals of copper sulphate are formed. When the solution is cooled slowly, larger and better-shaped crystals are formed.

Physical and chemical changes

Physical changes

Ice changing into water, water changing into steam and magnetising a piece of iron are some examples of physical changes. In each case, new properties may be gained, but there is no change in mass.

A **physical change** is a change in which no new substance is formed but the original substance gains new properties.

Chemical changes

Burning fuels, burning magnesium and rusting iron are examples of chemical changes.

A **chemical change** is a change in which at least one new substance is formed.

Physical changes	Chemical changes
No new substances are formed	One or more new substances are formed
No change in mass	A change in mass
Can be easily reversed	Not easily reversed
Often no heat is involved	Heat is usually involved

Examining Substances

- Is it a solid, liquid or gas?
- What colour is it?
- What kind of smell does it have?
- Is it an element?
- Is it a metal or a non-metal?
- Is it a compound?
- Is it a mixture?
- Is it a solution?
- Is it an acid or a base?
- Mixtures can be separated easily if the **physical properties** of the parts of the mixture are very different from each other.

Separating mixtures

Many substances are mixtures that may need to be separated. Crude oil is a mixture that is difficult to separate into gases such as methane, liquids such as petrol and tarry solids such as bitumen. Simple mixtures, such as seawater, can be separated easily into water and salt.

Separating techniques

- **Filtration** is used to separate small insoluble solids from a liquid. The filter paper has tiny holes that let the liquid through, but are too small to allow the solid particles through. Sand can be separated from water by filtration.
- **Evaporation** is used to separate a solid, a liquid or a gas from a mixture. Salt is obtained from a salt solution by heating the solution and allowing the water to evaporate, leaving the salt behind.
- **Crystallisation:** Solids can be separated from a concentrated solution by allowing them to crystallise.
- **Distillation is evaporation followed by condensation**. It is mainly used to separate miscible liquids that have different boiling points. It can also be used to separate solids from a solid and liquid mixture.
- **Chromatography** is used to separate small amounts of substances in a mixture. A small sample of colouring can be separated into different colours by paper chromatography.
- **Paper chromatography** is a method of separating substances by allowing a solvent to carry them different distances along a filter paper.

Mandatory experiment

(a) To separate a mixture of sand and water by filtration

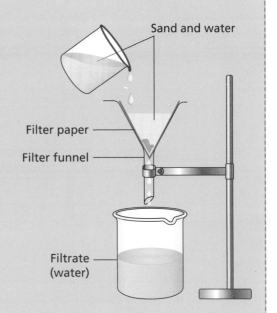

Sand and water

Filter paper

Filter funnel

Filtrate (water)

Procedure

1. Fold a piece of filter paper into the shape of a cone. Place it into a filter funnel.
2. Pour the mixture of sand and water through the filter.
3. Collect the clear water in a beaker.

Result

The water flows through the tiny holes in the filter paper. The sand particles are too large and cannot get through. The sand remains in the filter paper.

(b) To separate a mixture of salt and water by evaporation

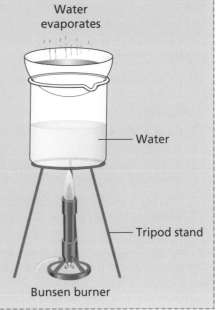

Water evaporates

Water

Tripod stand

Bunsen burner

Procedure

1. Make a salt solution by dissolving some salt (NaCl) in a beaker.
2. Pour some of the solution into a clean evaporating basin.
3. Heat the solution as shown in the diagram.

Result

The water evaporates, leaving the salt behind.

(c) To separate a mixture of alcohol and water by distillation

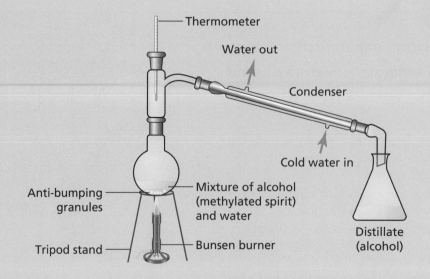

Procedure
1. Set up the apparatus as shown.
2. Turn on the water tap and allow water to flow through the condenser.
3. Heat the mixture of alcohol and water.
4. Collect the distillate (alcohol) in a conical flask.

Result

Alcohol flows out through the condenser and into the conical flask. The thermometer shows a steady temperature of 78°C – this is the boiling point of the alcohol.

(d) To separate a mixture of inks using paper chromatography

Procedure

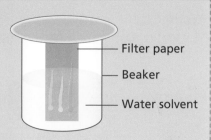

1. Pour a small amount of water into a glass trough or beaker.
2. Put a small spot from different coloured inks on a rectangular piece of filter paper.
3. Dip the paper into the water. Hang the paper as shown in the diagram.

Result

The water moves up through the paper by capillary action. The coloured inks that are soluble in water move up through the filter paper at different speeds.

Sample questions and answers

1. *A pupil measured the effect of temperature on the solubility of the salt ammonium chloride in water. The maximum mass of the salt that dissolved in 100 g of water is given at various temperatures in the table below. (Junior Cert 2007, Q5a)*

Grams of ammonium chloride in 100 g of water	29	37	46	55	66	77
Temperature (°C)	0	20	40	60	80	100

(a) *Plot a graph of solubility against temperature on the graph paper below.*

Answer

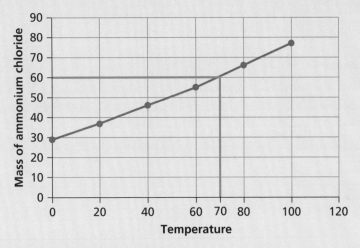

(b) *Use the graph to estimate the approximate solubility of ammonium chloride in water at 70°C.*

Answer

Solubility: Approximately 60 g of ammonium chloride dissolves in 100 g of water at 70°C.

2. *Pure water can be separated from a mixture of alcohol and water by* ***distillation***.

(a) *What is distillation?*

Answer

Distillation is evaporation followed by condensation.

(b) *Draw a labelled diagram of the apparatus used.*

Answer

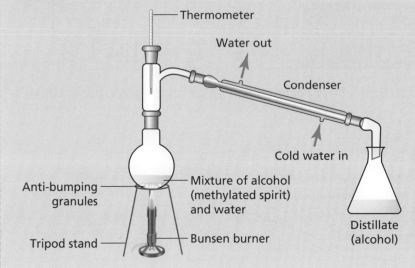

Thermometer

Water out

Condenser

Cold water in

Anti-bumping granules

Mixture of alcohol (methylated spirit) and water

Tripod stand

Bunsen burner

Distillate (alcohol)

18 Air, Oxygen and Carbon Dioxide

The atmosphere (air) is a mixture of gases.

Composition of Air

Gas	Percentage of air
Nitrogen (N_2)	78
Oxygen (O_2)	21
Carbon dioxide (CO_2)	0.04
Water vapour (H_2O)	Small amount – varies
Noble gases	Small amount

The amount of water vapour in the air varies from day to day and from place to place. The air around us is a vital resource – oxygen is necessary for breathing, while carbon dioxide is necessary for photosynthesis.

Mandatory experiment

(a) To show that air contains approximately 21 per cent oxygen

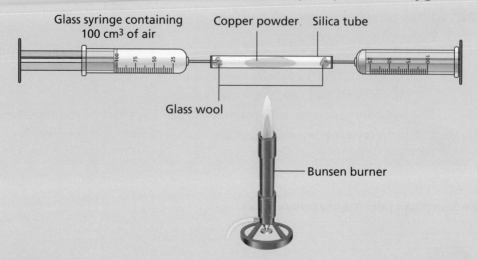

Glass syringe containing 100 cm³ of air — Copper powder — Silica tube — Glass wool — Bunsen burner

Procedure

1. Set up the apparatus as shown in the diagram.
2. Allow 100 cm³ of air into one syringe.
3. Do not allow any air into the second syringe.
4. Push the air backwards and forwards from one syringe to the other over the heated copper.
5. Remove the heat from the copper when the volume of air remains steady.

Result

Volume of air after heating = 79 cm³ (79 per cent).

Conclusion

The percentage of oxygen in air = 21 per cent.

(b) To show that air contains carbon dioxide

Procedure

1. Set up the apparatus as shown in the diagram.
2. Place some limewater into the test tube.
3. Use a suction pump to draw some air through the limewater.

Result

As air is drawn through, the limewater turns milky.

Conclusion

Air contains carbon dioxide.

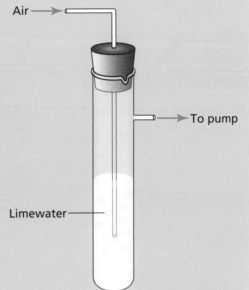

Air

To pump

Limewater

(c) To show that air contains water vapour

Procedure

1. Put a mixture of ice and salt into a test tube. Stopper the test tube.
2. Make sure that the outside is very dry.

Result

1. Drops of liquid condense on the cold surface.
2. When the liquid is added to anhydrous copper sulphate, it changes the copper sulphate powder blue.

Conclusion

Air contains water vapour.

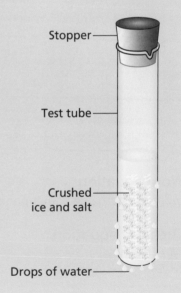

Stopper

Test tube

Crushed ice and salt

Drops of water

Oxygen – the reactive gas

Mandatory experiment

To prepare oxygen and examine its properties

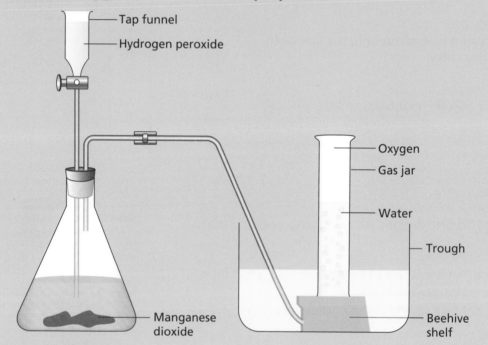

Word equation

hydrogen peroxide + manganese dioxide (catalyst) $\Rightarrow$ oxygen + water

Chemical equation

$$2H_2O_2 \xrightarrow{MnO_2} O_2 + 2H_2O$$

Procedure

1. Set up the apparatus as shown in the diagram.
2. Add the hydrogen peroxide solution slowly to the manganese dioxide.
3. Collect a total of five gas jars of the oxygen gas.

A **catalyst** is a substance that changes the speed of a chemical reaction.

(a) Test for oxygen: a glowing splint relights

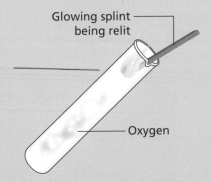

Glowing splint
being relit

Oxygen

(b) Burning carbon (charcoal) in oxygen

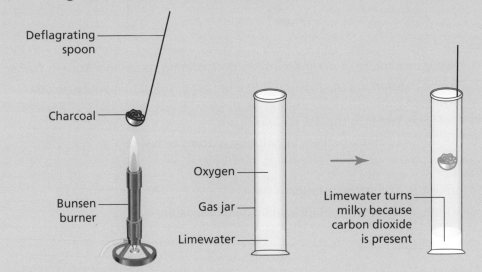

Deflagrating
spoon

Charcoal

Oxygen

Gas jar

Limewater

Bunsen
burner

Limewater turns
milky because
carbon dioxide
is present

Procedure

1. Heat a small piece of charcoal in a deflagrating spoon in a Bunsen flame.
2. Plunge the burning charcoal into a gas jar of oxygen.
3. Add some water to the gas jar and shake.
4. Use litmus to test whether the solution is acidic or basic.
5. Repeat steps 1 and 2. Add limewater to the gas jar.

Result

1. The litmus turns red: the solution is acidic.

   carbon + oxygen $\Rightarrow$ carbon dioxide **(acidic oxide)**
2. The limewater turns milky: carbon dioxide is present.

(c) Burning magnesium in oxygen

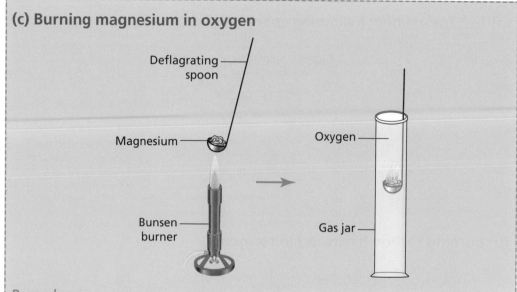

Procedure

1. Heat a small piece of magnesium in a deflagrating spoon in a Bunsen flame.
2. Plunge the burning magnesium into a gas jar of oxygen. A white powder forms.
3. Add some water to the gas jar and shake.
4. Use litmus to test whether the solution is acidic or basic.

Result

The litmus turns blue: the solution is basic.

magnesium + oxygen ⇒ magnesium oxide **(basic oxide)**

Properties and uses of oxygen

Physical properties	Chemical properties	Uses
Colourless, odourless, tasteless gas	Does not burn but supports combustion	Breathing
Slightly soluble in water	No effect on litmus	Welding and cutting
Slightly heavier than air	Reacts with metals and with non-metals to form oxides	Steel making

Carbon dioxide

Mandatory experiment

To prepare carbon dioxide and examine its properties

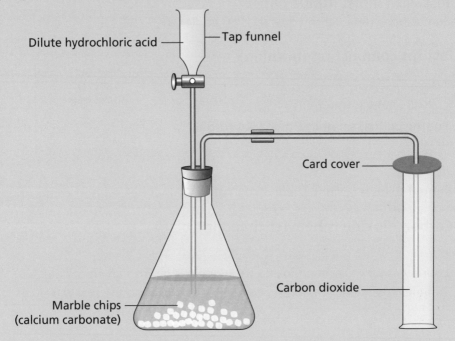

Dilute hydrochloric acid — Tap funnel

Card cover

Carbon dioxide

Marble chips
(calcium carbonate)

Word equation

calcium carbonate + hydrochloric acid ⟹ calcium chloride + water
+ carbon dioxide

Chemical equation

$$CaCO_3 + 2\,HCl \Rightarrow CaCl_2 + H_2O + CO_2$$

Procedure

1. Set up the apparatus as shown in the diagram.
2. Add dilute hydrochloric acid slowly to the marble chips.
3. Collect five jars of the gas.

(a) Test for carbon dioxide: limewater turns milky

Word equation

calcium hydroxide + carbon dioxide
⇒ calcium carbonate + water

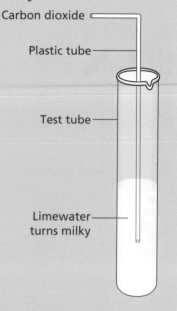

Carbon dioxide

Plastic tube

Test tube

Chemical equation
$$Ca(OH)_2 + CO_2 \Rightarrow CaCO_3 + H_2O$$

(b) Test with moist litmus paper
blue litmus turns red – carbon dioxide is an **acidic** gas.

(c) Test for combustion (burning)

Procedure

1. Light a wooden splint.
2. Put the lighted splint in a gas jar of carbon dioxide.

Limewater turns milky

Result

The lighted splint is extinguished: carbon dioxide does not support combustion.

(d) Carbon dioxide is heavier than air

Procedure

1. Pour a gas jar of carbon dioxide from one gas jar into an empty gas jar.
2. Test each gas jar for the presence of carbon dioxide using limewater.

Result

The limewater turns milky in the gas jar into which the carbon dioxide was poured. The gas jar that originally contained the carbon dioxide does not turn the limewater milky.

Conclusion

Carbon dioxide is heavier than air.

Properties and uses of carbon dioxide

Physical properties	Chemical properties	Uses
Colourless, odourless, tasteless gas	Does not support combustion	Fire extinguishers
Slightly soluble in water	Acidic – turns blue litmus red	Fizzy drinks
Heavier than air	Turns limewater milky	Fridges

Sample questions and answers

1. *Oxygen can be prepared by decomposing a liquid using a solid catalyst. (Junior Cert 2009, Q5a)*

   (a) *Name the liquid used.*

   Answer

   Hydrogen peroxide.

   (b) *Name the catalyst.*

   Answer

   Manganese dioxide.

   (c) *What is a catalyst?*

   Answer

   A catalyst is a substance that changes the speed of a chemical reaction.

2. *Carbon was burned in oxygen and the products were tested with pieces of moist red and blue litmus paper. Give the result of the litmus test described and make a conclusion based on this result.*

   Answer

   Result: The moist blue litmus paper turned red in colour.

   Conclusion: The products tested were acidic.

3. *When a mixture of ice and salt are put into a clean test tube, drops of liquid condense on the outside of the test tube. How would you confirm that the drops of liquid are water?*

   Answer

   When the liquid is added to anhydrous copper sulphate, it changes the copper sulphate from white to blue.

   or

   When the liquid is added to cobalt chloride paper, it changes the cobalt chloride paper from blue to pink.

   > The use of cobalt chloride paper to test for water is being discontinued on health and safety grounds. It will still be used in examination questions. Anhydrous copper sulphate should be used instead to test for water. When water drops fall on anhydrous copper sulphate it turns blue.

19 Water

aims **In this chapter you need to learn:**

1. Some properties of water.
2. How water is purified at a waterworks.
3. How hard water is removed.
4. Mandatory experiment: To show that water contains dissolved solids.
5. Mandatory experiment:
   (a) To test water for hardness.
   (b) To obtain a sample of pure water from seawater.
   (c) The decomposition of water by electrolysis.
6. How water is broken into hydrogen and oxygen by electrolysis.

Water is the most common liquid on earth. All living things need water to survive. We use water every day of our lives – to drink, to wash, to get rid of waste. Water is more important than food – we can survive for weeks without food, but for only a few days without water.

Properties of water

- **Water is a compound.** It is a molecule made up of one oxygen atom joined to two hydrogen atoms.
- **Water exists as a solid, as a liquid and as a gas on earth.** It melts at 0°C and boils at 100°C.

- **Water expands as it freezes.** This means that **ice is less dense than water**. Ice floats on water and acts as an insulator and prevents the water below from freezing.
- **Water is an excellent solvent.** Almost everything dissolves in water to some extent.
- **Water has high surface tension.** It seems to have a skin on its surface. This allows a needle to float on water and insects to walk on water.
- **Water rises up narrow tubes.** This is called **capillarity**. This allows water to rise up through plants.

Tests for water

- Water turns anhydrous copper sulphate blue.
- Water turns cobalt chloride paper from blue to pink.

The water cycle

Water supplies are constantly renewed by a cycle of evaporation from the earth and rain from the clouds in the atmosphere.

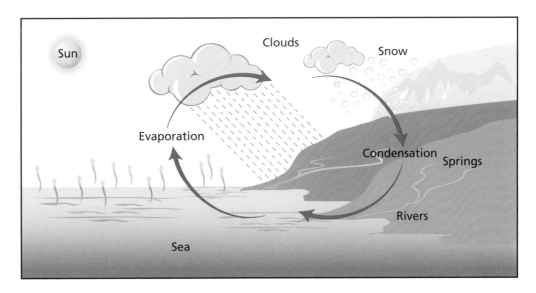

Heat from the sun causes evaporation from rivers, lakes and seas. The vapour condenses and forms clouds. These clouds cool and form large droplets that can fall as rain, hail, sleet or snow.

Water treatment

It is possible to drink rainwater. Water flowing over land may pick up all sorts of solids, liquids, bacteria and parasites that may cause sickness or give a nasty taste or smell. Water purified at a waterworks makes it fit to drink.

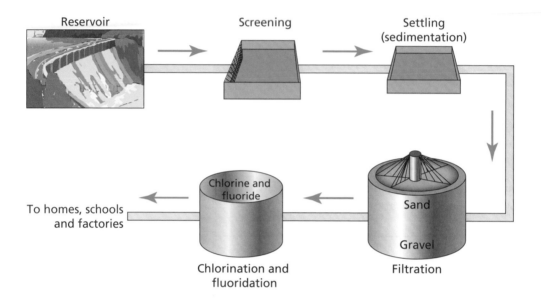

1. **Screening:** Water is passed through a mesh to remove floating debris, such as plastic bags and wood.
2. **Settling:** Aluminium sulphate is added to the water. This allows the tiny suspended solids to stick together and form large clumps that settle on the bottom of the settling tank.
3. **Filtration:** Water is filtered through filter beds consisting of gravel and fine sand.
4. **Chlorination:** Chlorine is added to kill the bacteria in the water.
5. **Fluoridation:** Some countries, such as Ireland, are obliged by law to add fluoride to the water to help prevent tooth decay.

Water hardness

- **Soft water** forms a lather easily with soap.
- **Hard water** does not easily form a lather with soap. It forms a scum.

The **calcium ions** found in many rocks dissolve in water. These calcium ions react with the soap to form a scum.

Advantages and disadvantages of hard water

Advantages	Disadvantages
Nicer taste	Blocks pipes
Good for brewing	Wastes soap
Provides calcium	Produces scum

soap + Ca^{2+} ions = scum

Removal of hardness

Hardness in water can be removed by **boiling, distillation and by ion exchange**. Water softeners contain ion exchange resins.

Removal of hard water by ion exchange

Allow the hard water to run through the ion exchange resin. The ions that cause hardness in water (Ca^{2+} ions) are exchanged by ions in the resin that do not cause hardness in water (usually Na^+ ions).

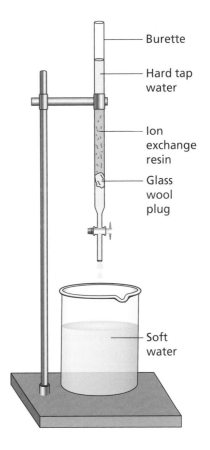

Burette

Hard tap water

Ion exchange resin

Glass wool plug

Soft water

Mandatory experiment

To show that water contains dissolved solids

Procedure

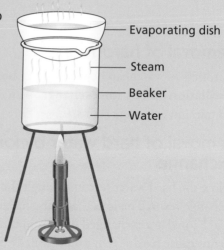

1. Collect a number of water samples – tap water, river water, seawater and spring water.

2. Filter one of the samples (tap water) through filter paper. This will remove any suspended solids.

3. Place approximately 100 cm³ of the water sample into a clean evaporating dish.

4. Heat the water on a water bath as shown.

5. Turn off the heat when all the water in the evaporating dish has evaporated.

6. Repeat steps 2 to 5 using different water samples.

Evaporating dish

Steam

Beaker

Water

Result

A solid is left in the evaporating dish.

Conclusion

Water contains dissolved solids. Different water samples contain different amounts of dissolved solids.

Mandatory experiment

(a) To test water for hardness

Different water samples – spring water, tap water, seawater and hard water – are tested with soap solution (or soap flakes) to see how easily they form a lather.

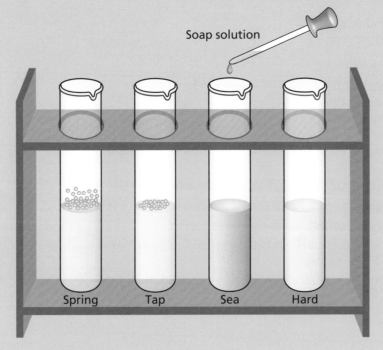

Soap solution

Spring   Tap   Sea   Hard

Procedure

1. Place 10 cm³ of each water sample into four test tubes.
2. Add soap solution to each sample, 1 cm³ each time.
3. Shake each test tube until a lather forms. If no lather forms, add more soap solution.
4. Measure the amount of soap solution necessary to form a lather.

Results

The hard water and the seawater do not form a lather easily. The tap water and the spring water are soft. However, they can be hard or soft, depending on the types of rocks in your locality.

(b) To obtain a sample of pure water from seawater

Procedure

1. Set up the apparatus as shown.

2. Turn on the water tap and allow water to flow through the condenser.

3. Heat the seawater.

4. Collect the distillate (water) in a conical flask.

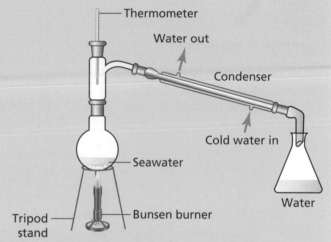

Result

Water flows out through the condenser and into the conical flask. The thermometer shows a steady temperature of 100°C – this is the boiling point of the water. The salt remains in the round-bottomed flask.

(c) The decomposition of water by electrolysis

1. Hydrogen gas collects at the negative electrode. When lighted, it 'pops'.

2. Oxygen gas collects at the positive electrode. It relights a glowing splint.

3. Water is a compound of hydrogen and oxygen. Twice as much hydrogen as oxygen is produced.

4. Water (H_2O) contains two atoms of hydrogen and one atom of oxygen.

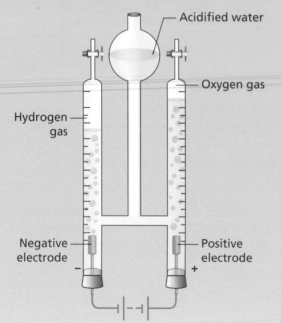

key point

Electrolysis is the chemical breakdown of an electrolyte when an electric current is passed through it.

Sample questions and answers

1. *Water supplied to domestic consumers has undergone five or more different processes in a water treatment plant. (Junior Cert 2007, Q6d)*

   (a) *Name any five of the processes carried out on water in a treatment plant.*

   Answer

   Screening, settling, filtration, chlorination and fluoridation.

   (b) *Why is chlorine added to water?*

   Answer

   To kill the bacteria present in water.

2. *How would you show that water contained dissolved solids?*

   Answer

   (i)   Filter the water sample through filter paper to remove any suspended solids.

   (ii) Place a sample of the filtered water into a clean evaporating dish.

   (iii) When the water evaporates, the dissolved solids remain in the evaporating dish.

3. *How is hard water removed by ion exchange?*

   Answer

   The ions that cause hardness (Ca^{2+} ions) are exchanged for ions that do not cause hardness (usually Na^+ ions).

4. *State how you would test water to confirm the presence of hardness. (Junior Cert 2009, Q5b)*

   Answer

   When a large amount of soap solution is added to the water, it does not easily form a lather. It forms a scum.

 **20** Atomic Structure, Ionic and Covalent Bonding

 In this chapter you need to learn:

1. Atoms are made up of protons, neutrons and electrons.
2. The arrangements of electrons in atoms are called Bohr structures.
3. The number of electrons in the outer shell (orbit) of an atom helps explain how atoms combine with each other.
4. How ionic bonds and covalent bonds are formed and how they differ from each other.

Atoms

- Atoms are made up of small particles called **subatomic particles**.
- These are protons, neutrons and electrons.
- The mass of a proton and a neutron are the same: 1 atomic mass unit (amu).
- The mass of an electron is so small compared to a proton (1/1,840) or neutron that we do not count its mass.
- **Protons are positive (+), electrons are negative (−) and neutrons are neutral.**

Particle	Mass	Charge	Location
Proton	1	Positive	Nucleus
Electron	0	Negative	Electron cloud
Neutron	1	Neutral	Nucleus

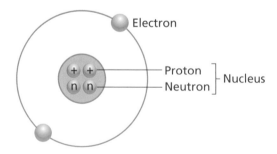

 key point

In an atom, **the number of protons (+) = the number of electrons (−).**

Arrangement of electrons in atoms

- **Electrons move around the nucleus in orbits.**
- Each orbit can hold a certain number of electrons.
- The first orbit is full when it contains **two** electrons, the next orbit is full when it contains **eight** electrons and the next orbit is full when it contains **eight** electrons.

- **Atomic (proton) number** is the number of protons (or electrons) in an atom of an element.
- **Mass number** is the number of protons and neutrons in an atom of an element.

Bohr structures

Atoms with full orbits (shells).

2
He
4

10
Ne
20

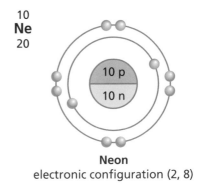

Helium
electronic configuration (2)

Neon
electronic configuration (2, 8)

Some other atoms:

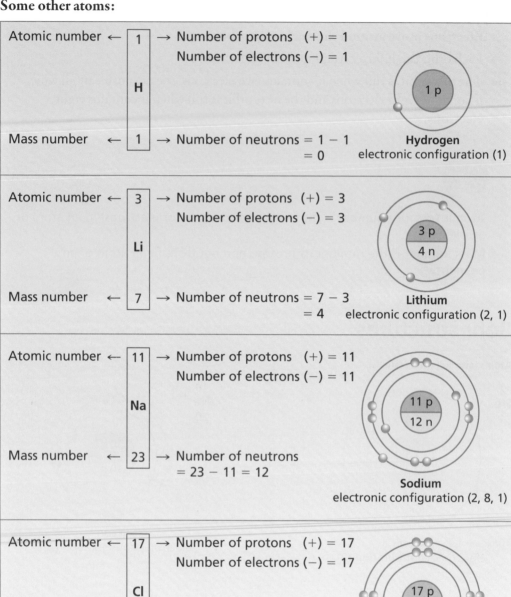

Atomic number ← 1 → Number of protons (+) = 1
Number of electrons (−) = 1

H

Mass number ← 1 → Number of neutrons = 1 − 1
= 0

Hydrogen
electronic configuration (1)

Atomic number ← 3 → Number of protons (+) = 3
Number of electrons (−) = 3

Li

Mass number ← 7 → Number of neutrons = 7 − 3
= 4

Lithium
electronic configuration (2, 1)

Atomic number ← 11 → Number of protons (+) = 11
Number of electrons (−) = 11

Na

Mass number ← 23 → Number of neutrons
= 23 − 11 = 12

Sodium
electronic configuration (2, 8, 1)

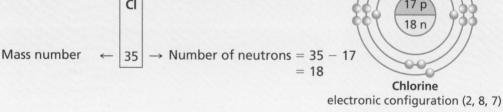

Atomic number ← 17 → Number of protons (+) = 17
Number of electrons (−) = 17

Cl

Mass number ← 35 → Number of neutrons = 35 − 17
= 18

Chlorine
electronic configuration (2, 8, 7)

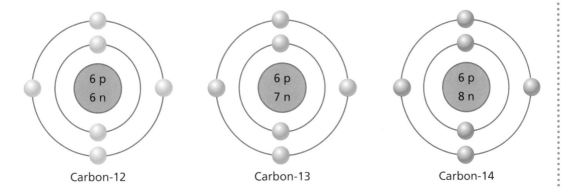

| Carbon-12 | Carbon-13 | Carbon-14 |

Chemical bonds

- Atoms combine with each other to form compounds.
- When they join with each other, **they try to have full outer shells** (either two or eight electrons).
- Atoms combine with each other by forming chemical bonds.
- A chemical bond is the 'glue' that holds a compound together.
- **Ionic bonds and covalent bonds** are the main types of chemical bond.

Ionic bonding

- An **ion** is an electrically charged atom or group of atoms.
- Positive ions are formed by the **loss** of electrons. Negative ions are formed by **gaining** electrons.
- An ionic bond is formed by the **attractive force between a positive and a negative ion**.
- Ionic compounds are formed when elements from **the left-hand side (+) and the right-hand side of the periodic table (−) combine.**

An **ionic bond** is formed when **electrons are transferred** between atoms.

HL Sodium chloride (NaCl)

- Sodium has **one electron** in its outer shell, which it wants to **lose** in order to have a full outer orbit.
- Chlorine has **seven electrons** in its outer shell – it needs to **gain** one electron in order to have a full outer shell.
- Sodium reacts with chlorine by **transferring the one electron** in its outer shell to chlorine.
- The sodium atom becomes a positive ion and the chlorine atom becomes a negative ion. These **oppositely charged ions attract** each other and form the compound sodium chloride.

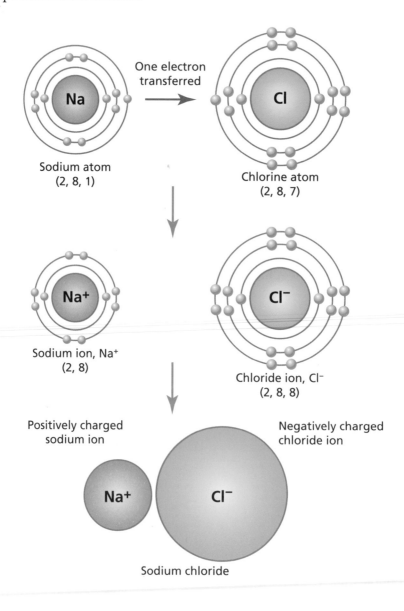

One electron transferred

Sodium atom
(2, 8, 1)

Chlorine atom
(2, 8, 7)

Sodium ion, Na⁺
(2, 8)

Chloride ion, Cl⁻
(2, 8, 8)

Positively charged
sodium ion

Negatively charged
chloride ion

Na⁺   Cl⁻

Sodium chloride

Magnesium oxide (MgO)

- Magnesium has **two electrons** in its outer shell.
- Oxygen has **six electrons** in its outer shell.
- Magnesium reacts with oxygen by **transferring two electrons** to oxygen.
- The magnesium atom becomes a positive ion and the oxygen atom becomes a negative ion. These **oppositely charged ions** attract each other and form magnesium oxide.

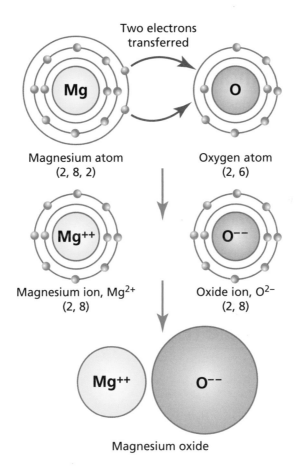

Two electrons
transferred

Magnesium atom
(2, 8, 2)

Oxygen atom
(2, 6)

Magnesium ion, Mg^{2+}
(2, 8)

Oxide ion, O^{2-}
(2, 8)

Magnesium oxide

Covalent bonding

- Not all atoms want to transfer electrons from one to the other. Some non-metals share electrons with each other. In this way, they can obtain full outer shells (two electrons or eight electrons).
- Covalent bonding involves the **valence (outer) electrons only.**
- **Covalent molecules** are formed when elements from the **right-hand side (−) of the periodic table (−) combine with each other. (Non-metals** combine with non-metals.)

A **covalent bond** is formed by the sharing of electrons between atoms.

HL The hydrogen molecule (H₂)

- A hydrogen atom has one electron in its outer shell. Hydrogen needs two electrons to have a full outer shell.
- When two hydrogen atoms come close enough to each other, their outer shells overlap and they share a pair of electrons. Each hydrogen atom is in a stable state because each has two electrons in its outer shell.
- This sharing of electrons is called a covalent bond.

The water molecule (H₂O)

- An oxygen atom has six electrons in its outer shell. Oxygen needs eight electrons to have a full outer shell.
- When an oxygen atom comes close enough to two hydrogen atoms, their outer shells overlap and oxygen shares a pair of electrons with each hydrogen atom.
- The oxygen atom is in a stable state because each has eight electrons in its outer shell, while at the same time each hydrogen atom is in a stable state because they have two electrons in their outer shells.

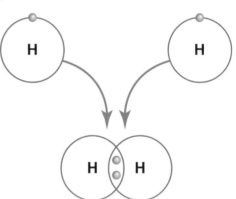

Only the electrons in the outer shell are involved in the bonding

Oxygen atom, O

Hydrogen atom, H

Hydrogen atom, H

The electrons in the inner shell do not play a part in the bonding

The methane molecule (CH₄)

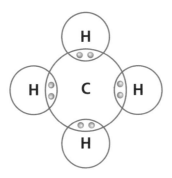

To investigate the ability of ionic and covalent substances to conduct electricity

Procedure

1. Set up the test circuit as shown in the diagram.
2. Test the following substances: water, alcohol, sugar solution, salt solution, copper sulphate solution and dilute hydrochloric acid.

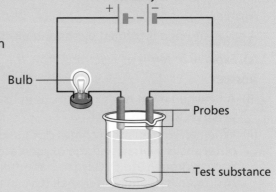

Results

Ionic solutions	Covalent substances	
Conducts electricity	Conducts electricity	Non-conductors
Salt solution	Dilute hydrochloric acid	Water
Copper sulphate solution		Alcohol
		Sugar solution

Conclusion

Solutions that contain ions conduct electricity. Ionic substances break up into ions in water. Most covalent compounds do not conduct electricity. HCl (a covalent compound) dissolves in water and forms ions. Therefore, dilute HCl can conduct electricity.

Properties of ionic and covalent compounds

Ionic	Covalent
Usually crystalline solids	Usually liquids or gases
High melting points and boiling points	Low melting points and boiling points
Consist of giant lattices	Consist of separate molecules
Usually soluble in water	Usually insoluble in water
Conduct electricity when melted or in solution	Most do not conduct electricity

Sample questions and answers

1. (a) *Name the type of bonding in the water molecule. (Junior Cert 2009, Q6a)*

   Answer

   Covalent bonding.

   (b) *Describe this type of bond.*

   Answer

   A covalent bond is formed by sharing electrons between atoms.

   (c) *Explain, in terms of electrons, how the water molecule is formed.*

   Answer

   (i) An oxygen atom has six electrons in its outer shell. Hydrogen has one electron in its outer shell.

   (ii) When an oxygen atom comes close enough to two hydrogen atoms, their outer shells overlap and the oxygen atom shares a pair of electrons with each hydrogen atom. Oxygen has a full outer shell (eight electrons) and hydrogen has a full outer shell (two electrons).

2. (a) *How are sodium ions and chloride ions formed from their atoms? (Junior Cert 2009, Q6b)*

   Answer

   The sodium atom (Na) (2, 8, 1) loses one electron to become a sodium ion (Na^+) (2, 8). The chlorine atom (Cl) (2, 8, 7) gains one electron to become a chloride ion (Cl^-) (2, 8, 8).

   (b) *What force holds the ions together in sodium chloride?*

   Answer

   An ionic bond (or electrostatic attraction or coulombic force).

   (c) *Name and give the formulas of some other compounds that are composed of ions.*

   Answer

   Magnesium oxide (MgO).
   Calcium chloride ($CaCl_2$).
   Sodium hydroxide (NaOH).

21 Acids and Bases

In this chapter you need to learn:

1. The properties and some reactions of acids and bases.
2. How indicators are used to test whether a substance is an acid, a base or neutral.
3. The pH scale and how it is used to find the pH of different substances.
4. Mandatory experiment: To titrate hydrochloric acid against sodium hydroxide and prepare a sample of sodium chloride.
5. The names and formulas of some acids and bases.

Acids

Acids are usually recognised by simple properties such as taste, how they react with indicators and how they react with each other. Some acids, such as hydrochloric acid, nitric acid and sulphuric acid, are very dangerous – they attack metals, stone, clothing and flesh. Other acids, like carbonic acid in soft drinks, lactic acid in milk and citric acid in fruits, are not dangerous.

Properties of acids

- Acids have a sour taste. Vinegar and citric acids have a stinging sour taste.

- Acids are corrosive. Acids attack metals, stone, materials and flesh.

Acids turn blue litmus red.

- Acids have a pH less than 7. Strong acids such as hydrochloric acid have a pH close to 0, while weak acids like milk are close to 7.

- Most acids react with most metals to form salts and release hydrogen gas.
  metal + acid $\Rightarrow$ salt + hydrogen

- Acids react with carbonates to produce carbon dioxide gas.
  carbonate + acid $\Rightarrow$ salt + carbon dioxide + water

- Acids neutralise bases by forming a salt and water. This is called neutralisation.
  acid + base $\Rightarrow$ salt + water

Bases

- Bases are the opposite of acids.
- **Bases that are soluble in water are called alkalis.** Alkalis are soapy to touch because they react with the natural oils on the skin to make soap.
- Bases are corrosive.
- Bases have a pH greater than 7. Ammonia has a pH close to 7, while sodium hydroxide has a pH closer to 14.
- Ammonia, metal hydroxides and metal oxides are bases.
- Bases neutralise acids by forming a salt and water.

Bases turn red litmus blue.

Neutralisation

When an acid is mixed with a base, they react with each other and cancel each other out by forming a salt and water. This is called **neutralisation**.

acid + base ⟹ salt + water

Examples

Word equation

hydrochloric acid + sodium hydroxide ⟹ sodium chloride + water

Chemical equation

$HCl + NaOH \Rightarrow NaCl + H_2O$

Word equation

hydrochloric acid + calcium carbonate ⟹ calcium chloride + carbon dioxide + water

Chemical equation

$2HCl + CaCl_2 \Rightarrow CaCl_2 + CO_2 + H_2O$

Indicators are substances that change colour depending on whether they are in an acidic or alkaline solution.

- Litmus indicator is red in acid and blue in base.
- Universal indicator is a mixture of indicators.

Using indicators to test whether a substance is acidic, basic or neutral

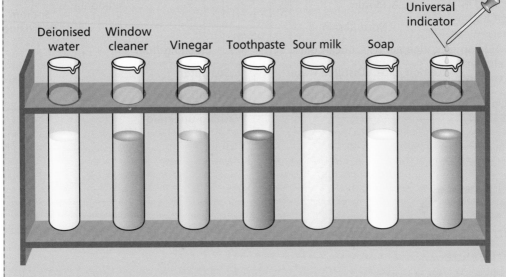

Deionised water | Window cleaner | Vinegar | Toothpaste | Sour milk | Soap | Universal indicator

Procedure

1. Place samples of a number of substances in test tubes.
2. Add a drop of universal indicator to each sample.
3. Compare the colour obtained with the colour on the colour chart.

Results

Acidic	Basic	Neutral
Vinegar	Window cleaner	Deionised water
Sour milk	Toothpaste solution	
Soap solution		

The pH scale

An indicator can tell us only whether a substance is an acid or a base. If we want to know the measure of the acidity or basicity, we use a scale called the pH scale. The scale goes from 0 to 14.

key point

On the pH scale:
- Acids are less than 7.
- Neutral solutions like water are equal to 7.
- Bases are greater than 7.

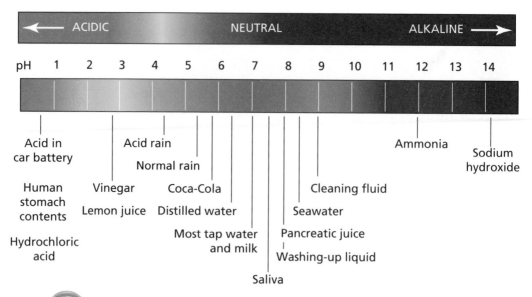

To find the pH of different substances

Procedure

1. Place samples of a number of substances in test tubes.
2. Add a drop of universal indicator to each sample.
3. Compare the colour obtained with the colour on the colour chart.
4. Write down the pH of each substance.

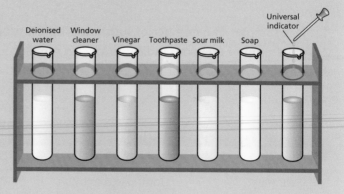

Substance	Acidic	Basic	Neutral	pH
Deionised water			x	7
Window cleaner		x		9
Vinegar	x			3
Toothpaste		x		9
Sour milk	x			3
Soap	x			6

Mandatory experiment

To titrate hydrochloric acid against sodium hydroxide and prepare a sample of sodium chloride

Procedure

1. Add exactly 25 cm³ of sodium hydroxide solution to the **conical flask** using a **pipette**.

2. Add two or three drops of methyl orange to the sodium hydroxide solution. The solution turns yellow.

3. Add hydrochloric acid solution from a **burette**, drop by drop, to the sodium hydroxide solution until the indicator changes from **yellow to red**. This is the end point – the sodium hydroxide has been neutralised by the hydrochloric acid.

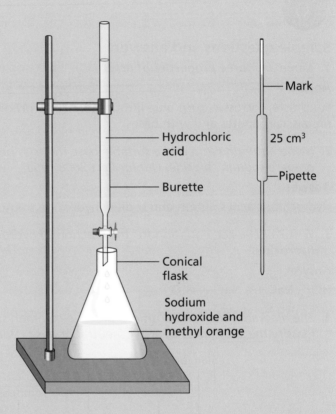

4. Note the volume of hydrochloric acid used.

5. Repeat the procedure without the indicator. Add exactly the same volume of hydrochloric acid solution as before.

6. Pour some of the contents of the conical flask into an evaporating dish.

7. Evaporate the water from the salt solution to obtain a dry sample of sodium chloride.

Some strong acids and bases

Acid	Formula	Base	Formula
Hydrochloric acid	HCl	Sodium hydroxide	NaOH
Sulphuric acid	H_2SO_4	Calcium hydroxide	$Ca(OH)_2$

Sample questions and answers

1. *Name any three properties of acids.*

Answer

Sour taste, corrosive, turn blue litmus red, have a pH of less than 7, react with metals, carbonates and with bases.

2. *Name a suitable acid and a suitable base that can be used in a titration to prepare sodium chloride. (Junior Cert 2006, Q5a)*

Answer

Hydrochloric acid solution and sodium hydroxide solution.

3. *Write a balanced equation for the reaction of hydrochloric acid and sodium hydroxide.*

Answer

$HCl + NaOH = NaCl + H_2O$

4. *The diagram shows the positions of some common substances on the pH scale. Classify the substances as acidic, neutral or basic. (Junior Cert 2008, Q6b)*

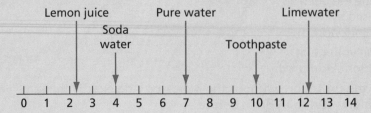

Answer

Acidic: Lemon juice and soda water.

Neutral: Pure water.

Basic: Toothpaste and limewater.

22 Fossil Fuels, Acid Rain and Plastics

 In this chapter you need to learn:
1. Fossil fuels.
2. How carbon dioxide reacts with water.
3. The difference between normal rain and acid rain.
4. Plastics are polymers.
5. The properties and uses of some common plastics.
6. Plastics are non-biodegradable.

Fossil fuels

Millions of years ago, much of the earth's surface was covered by sea, in which an abundance of marine plants and animals lived. As these organisms died, the dead material was converted into the many kinds of **hydrocarbon molecules** that make up **coal, crude oil and natural gas.** Fossil fuels are **non-renewable.**

Natural gas is a mixture of hydrocarbons. Natural gas is found in Ireland in the sea near Kinsale. It is composed of approximately 95 per cent methane (CH_4). It is also found in slurry pits, coalmines and refuse dumps.

Combustion of fossil fuels

HL

Fossil fuels are hydrocarbons and release energy when they are burned in oxygen.

fuel + $O_2 \Rightarrow CO_2 + H_2O$ + energy

Acid rain

Normal rainwater is slightly acidic. Carbon dioxide in the air reacts with the rainwater to form a weak acid called carbonic acid. This has a pH of about 5.5.

Word equation

carbon dioxide + water $\Rightarrow$ carbonic acid

Chemical equation

$CO_2 + H_2O \Rightarrow H_2CO_3$

Power stations, factories, motor vehicles and homes burn fuels that give off fumes into the atmosphere. These fumes contain **sulphur dioxide (SO_2)** and oxides of nitrogen (NO_x). These oxides react with rainwater and form sulphuric acid and nitric acid. **These strong acids lower the pH below the normal value of 5.5.**

Acid rain kills trees, damages crops, releases harmful metals into soil, destroys limestone buildings and harms aquatic species.

key point

> **Acid rain** is rainwater with a pH of less than that of normal rainwater (< 5.5).

Plastics

Plastics are giant molecules. Plastics are all around us – in pens, tapes, compact discs, bins, clothes, cars and many more items.

Plastics are **polymers**. Polymers are large chain-like molecules that are built up from smaller molecules called **monomers**. The word *polymer* comes from the Greek *poly*, meaning *many*, and *meros*, meaning *part*.

For example, polyethene is made up from many ethene molecules. The ethene molecules are joined together something **like a chain of paper clips**.

All living things are made from natural polymers like protein, starch and cellulose. Today we take polymers for granted, whether they are natural polymers such as rubber, silk and cotton or synthetic polymers such as plastics or fibres.

Polymers have widespread uses because they are strong, flexible, easy to shape and can often be tailor made to suit almost any purpose.

Some common plastics and their uses

Plastic	Property	Uses
Polythene	Easily moulded	Plastic packaging and squeezy bottles
Polypropylene	Hardwearing	Kitchenware and carpets
Polystyrene	Non-conductor of heat and electricity	Plastic cups and insulation
Teflon	Non-stick surface	Knee and hip joints and ski surfaces
PVC	Easily moulded	Pipes, gutters and floor covering

Plastics are **non-biodegradable.** This means that they do not rot away in the environment like wood. For this reason, plastics can cause litter problems. Plastics emit poisonous fumes when they are burned. Most countries **recycle** plastics to limit their impact on the environment.

Sample questions and answers

1. *Name the main pollutants emitted from a coal-burning power station. Describe its effect on the environment.*

Answer

Sulphur dioxide (SO_2) and the oxides of nitrogen (NO_x) react with water to form acid rain. Acid rain kills trees, damages crops, releases metals into soil, destroys limestone buildings and harms aquatic species.

2. *What are polymers?*

Answer

Polymers are large, chain-like molecules that are built up from smaller molecules called monomers.

3. *What is polythene made up of?*

Answer

Ethene molecules.

4. *Why is polythene used to make plastic packaging?*

Answer

It is lightweight, waterproof, durable and easily moulded into various shapes.

PHYSICS

23 Measurement, Density and Flotation

 In this chapter you need to learn:

1. All matter has mass and takes up space.
2. Mandatory experiments:
   (a) To find the density of regular-shaped solids.
   (b) To find the density of an irregular-shaped object (a stone).
   (c) To find the density of a liquid.
3. Flotation and density.

What is physics?

Physics is the study of the physical properties of substances. It involves the measurement of matter and energy.

Matter

- Matter can exist in three forms or states: solids, liquids and gases.
- Matter is interchangeable, i.e. water is a liquid, but at high temperatures it becomes steam, which is a gas. At low temperatures water becomes ice, which is a solid.

Matter is anything that has mass and takes up space.

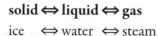

solid ⟺ liquid ⟺ gas

ice ⟺ water ⟺ steam

Measurement

The most important quantities measured in physics are **length, mass, temperature and time**. All other measurable quantities are related to these.

Instruments used in measurement

- An **opisometer** measures the length of curved lines.

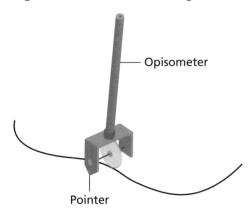

Opisometer

Pointer

- **Vernier calipers** measure the thickness or the diameter of a substance.
- **Weighing scales (laboratory balance)** measure the mass of a substance.
- A **thermometer** measures the temperature of a body.
- A **pendulum** measures time. The time of the swing depends on the length of the pendulum.

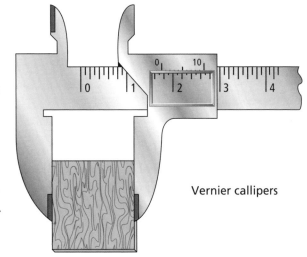

Vernier callipers

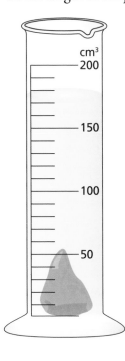

- A **graduated cylinder** measures the volume of a liquid. It can also be used to measure the volume of irregular solids.

SI units and symbols used in measurement

Quantity	Unit	Symbol	Other units used
Length	Metre	m	Kilometre (km), centimetre (cm), millimetre (mm)
Mass	Gram	g	Kilogram (kg)
Time	Second	s	Minutes, hours
Area	Square metre	m^2	Square centimetre (cm^2)
Volume	Cubic metre	m^3	Cubic centimetre (cm^3), litre (l)

Mass

All matter, whether it is a solid, a liquid or a gas, has mass. **Mass** is the amount of matter in a substance. It is measured in kilograms (kg).

Always use the correct units in all calculations.

Density

Is steel heavier than wood? The answer to this question depends on the quantities of each material. If we compare **equal volumes** of steel and wood, we find that steel has more mass, i.e. it is denser.

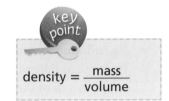

$$\text{density} = \frac{\text{mass}}{\text{volume}}$$

Example

A stone has a mass of 40 g and a volume of 10 cm³. What is its density?

$$\text{density} = \frac{\text{mass}}{\text{volume}} = \frac{40\,\text{g}}{10\,\text{cm}^3} = 4\,\text{g/cm}^3 \ (\text{or g cm}^{-3})$$

Mandatory experiment

To find the mass and volume of a variety of solids and liquids and hence find their densities

(a) To find the density of regular-shaped solids

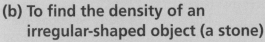

Procedure

1. Find the mass of the wooden block using a balance.

   mass = 12 g

2. Measure the length, width and height. Calculate the volume using the formula:

   V = l × w × h

   = 4 cm × 3 cm × 2 cm

   = 24 cm³

3. Calculate the density using the formula:

   $$density = \frac{mass}{volume} = \frac{12\ g}{24\ cm^3} = 0.5\ g\ cm^{-3}\ (or\ g/cm^3)$$

(b) To find the density of an irregular-shaped object (a stone)

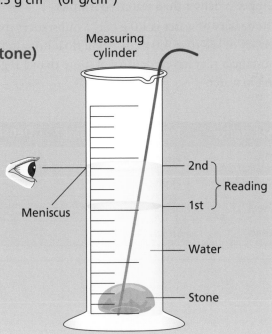

Measuring cylinder

Procedure

1. Find the mass of the stone using a balance.

   mass of stone = 51 g

2. Measure the rise in volume of the water when the stone is lowered carefully into the water. The rise in volume is the volume of the stone.

   volume of stone = 17 cm³

3. Use the formula:

   $$density = \frac{mass}{volume} = \frac{51\ g}{17\ cm^3}$$

   $$= 3\ g\ cm^{-3}\ (or\ g/cm^3)$$

(c) To find the density of a liquid

Procedure

1. Place a clean, dry, empty beaker on a balance. Set the reading back to zero using the tare button.

2. Using a pipette, place 100 cm³ of liquid in the beaker.

3. Find the mass of the liquid.

   mass of liquid = 80 g

4. Use the formula:

$$\text{density} = \frac{\text{mass}}{\text{volume}} = \frac{80 \text{ g}}{100 \text{ cm}^3}$$

$$= 0.8 \text{ g cm}^{-3} \text{ (or g/cm}^3\text{)}$$

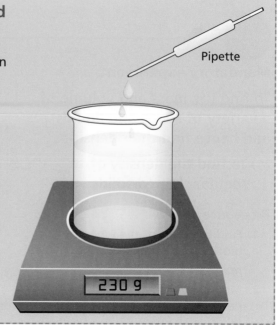

Pipette

230 g

HL Flotation and density

Cork is less dense than water, so it floats in water. Copper is denser than water, so it sinks.

The density of water is 1.0 g cm^{-3}. Substances that have a density of less than 1.0 g cm^{-3} will float on water, while substances that have a density of more than 1.0 g cm^{-3} will sink in water.

key point

A body will **float** in a liquid if it is less dense than the liquid.

Substance	Does it float or sink?	Density (g cm⁻³)
Oil	Floats	0.8
Wood (oak)	Floats	0.65
Steel	Sinks	8.0
Lead	Sinks	11.2

Sample questions and answers

1. *A stone has a mass of 52 g and a volume of 13 cm³. What is its density?*

Answer

$$\text{density} = \frac{\text{mass}}{\text{volume}} = \frac{52 \text{ g}}{13 \text{ cm}^3} = 4 \text{ g/cm}^3 \text{ (or g cm}^{-3}\text{)}$$

2. *Lead has a density of 11.2 g cm⁻³. Water has a density of 1 g cm⁻³. Will lead float on water?*

Answer

Lead sinks in water because it is denser than water.

24 Speed, Velocity and Acceleration

aims **In this chapter you need to learn:**

1. The difference between speed and velocity.
2. The definitions of speed, velocity and acceleration.
3. How to draw and use distance/time graphs and velocity/time graphs.

Speed

The world's fastest athletes can run 100 m in less than 10 seconds. The average speed of the athlete is found by dividing the distance travelled by the time taken.

$$\text{speed} = \frac{\text{distance}}{\text{time}} = \frac{100 \text{ m}}{10 \text{ s}} = 10 \text{ m/s (or } 10 \text{ m s}^{-1})$$

key point

Speed is the rate of change of distance with time.

HL Velocity

Like speed, velocity is measured in metres per second (m/s or m s^{-1}). It tells us the speed that something is travelling at, but it also tells us the direction in which it is travelling. For example, an athlete is running with a velocity of 17 m s^{-1} due south.

key point

Velocity is speed in a given direction.

Distance/time graphs

Distance/time graphs are used to calculate velocity.

When an object is **stationary**, the distance travelled does not change with time. Therefore, velocity = 0 m s^{-1}.

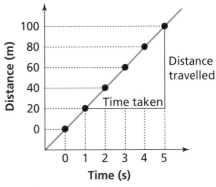

Time (s)	0	1	2	3	4	5
Distance (m)	0	20	40	60	80	100

When an object is moving at **constant velocity**, the speed remains the same.

$$\text{velocity} = \frac{\text{distance}}{\text{time}} = \frac{100 \text{ m}}{5 \text{ s}} = 20 \text{ m s}^{-1} \text{ (or 20 m/s)}$$

Acceleration

$$\text{acceleration} = \frac{\text{change in velocity}}{\text{time taken}}$$

When an object increases its velocity, it is accelerating. When it decreases its velocity, it is decelerating.

Acceleration is the change in velocity divided by the time taken.

Example

A car takes 10 seconds to change its velocity from 20 m s^{-1} to 50 m s^{-1}. What is its acceleration?

$$\text{acceleration} = \frac{\text{change in velocity}}{\text{time taken}} = \frac{50 \text{ m s}^{-1} - 20 \text{ m s}^{-1}}{10 \text{ s}} = \frac{30 \text{ m s}^{-1}}{10 \text{ s}} = 3 \text{ m s}^{-2}$$

We say that the car has an acceleration of 3 metres per second per second (3 m/s/s). This is usually written as 3 m/s^2 or as 3 m s^{-2}.

Example

A car starts from rest with a constant acceleration of 5 m s^{-2}. How long will it take to reach a speed of 30 m s^{-1}?

$$\text{acceleration} = \frac{\text{change in velocity}}{\text{time taken}}$$

$$5 \text{ m s}^{-2} = \frac{30 \text{ m s}^{-1} - 0}{t}$$

$$t = \frac{30 \text{ m s}^{-1}}{5 \text{ m s}^{-2}} = 6 \text{ seconds}$$

Velocity/time graphs are used to calculate acceleration.

Time (s)	0	1	2	3	4	5
Velocity (m/s)	0	5	10	15	20	25

The object is accelerating at 5 m s^{-2} (5 m/s/s).

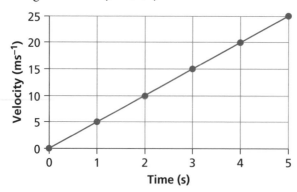

Sample questions and answers

1. *A stone was dropped from a cliff. The stone's approximate velocity was measured each second as it fell. The data collected during this experiment is given in the table below. Draw a graph of the data collected. (Junior Cert 2009, Q9c)*

Velocity (m s^{-1})	0	10	20	30	40	50
Time (seconds)	0	1	2	3	4	5

Answer

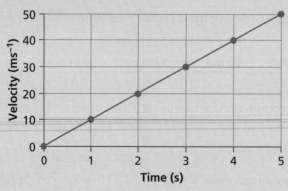

2. *Use the data to estimate the acceleration of the stone as it fell.*

Answer

$$\text{acceleration} = \frac{\text{change in velocity}}{\text{time taken}} = \frac{30 \text{ m s}^{-1} - 20 \text{ m s}^{-1}}{1 \text{ s}} = \frac{10 \text{ m s}^{-1}}{1 \text{ s}} = 10 \text{ m s}^{-2}$$

3. *The stone has a mass of 2 kg. What is the weight of the stone on earth?*

Answer

weight = mass × acceleration (See p. 142)

= 2 kg × 10 m s^{-2}

= 20 kg m s^{-2}

= 20 N

25 Forces, Levers and Moments of a Force

aims **In this chapter you need to learn:**

1. Force.
2. The difference between mass and weight.
3. Friction is a force.
4. Mandatory experiment: To investigate the relationship between the extension of a spring and the applied force (Hooke's law).
5. How levers work.
6. How the centre of gravity determines the stability of objects.

Forces

key point

A **force** is anything that tries to change the shape, direction or velocity of a body.

There are many different types of forces: pushing, pulling, bending, squeezing, twisting, stretching, etc. One of the most important forces is the pull of gravity, which we call weight.

Force is measured in newtons (N).

Weight

Sometimes people mix up weight and mass.

Mass and weight are related by the force of gravity.

key point

Weight is the gravitational force from the earth. It is measured in newtons (N).

Mass = 70 kg

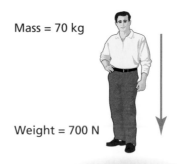

key point

weight = mass × g
(where g is the gravitational force = 10 N/kg)

weight = mass × 10 N/kg
= 70 kg × 10 N/kg
= 700 N

i.e. a person with a mass of 70 kg weighs 700 N.

Weight = 700 N

Earth

Example

An object weighs 600 N on earth. What is its weight when it is moved to the moon, where the acceleration due to gravity (g) is one-sixth of the earth's?

$$\text{weight on moon} = \frac{\text{weight on earth}}{6}$$

$$= \frac{600 \text{ N}}{6} = 100 \text{ N}$$

Friction

When two objects come in contact with each other, they experience a force. Rubbing your hands together, sliding on ice and scraping paint off glass are all examples of friction.

key point

Friction is a force that stops things from sliding over each other.

- Friction is used to slow cars down when the brakes come into contact with the wheels.

- Friction is reduced in cars by designing them to resist air flow.

- Friction is reduced in cars and other machines by lubrication with oil or grease.

key point

Hooke's law: The extension of a spring is directly proportional to the force that caused the extension.

Mandatory experiment

To investigate the relationship between the extension of a spring and the applied force

Procedure

1. Set up the apparatus as shown.
2. Place a mass on the pan to make the spring taut.
3. Note the reading on the metre stick.
4. Add a force of 5 N. Note the new reading on the metre stick.
5. Find the extension by subtracting the old reading from the new.
6. Continue to add more weights. Note the extension in each case.
7. Make a table of your results. Plot a graph of extension against force.

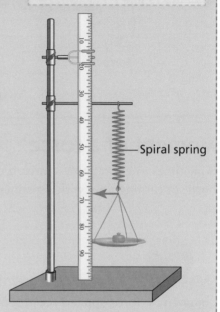

Spiral spring

Results

Force (N)	Extension (cm)
5	1
10	2
15	3
20	4
25	5

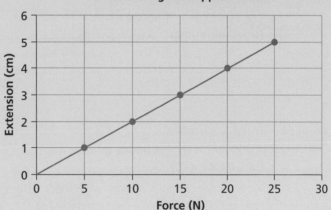

Extension against applied force

Conclusion

The graph is a straight line through the origin (0, 0). This shows that the extension is proportional to the force that caused it.

Levers

A door, a wheelbarrow, a seesaw and a spanner are all examples of levers. Levers make it easier to turn and twist things.

Fulcrum

Force

Moment of a force

Sometimes when we apply a force, it causes an object to turn or twist, e.g. opening a bottle or turning a nut with a spanner. The turning effect of a force is called a **moment**.

key point

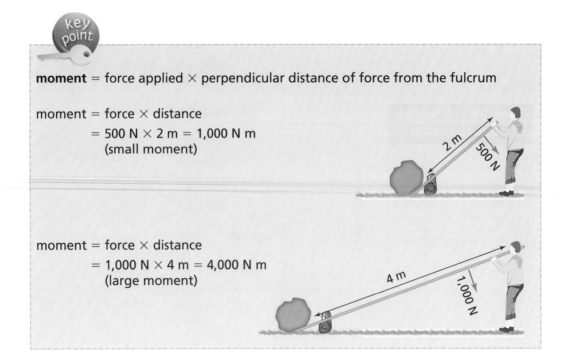

moment = force applied × perpendicular distance of force from the fulcrum

moment = force × distance
= 500 N × 2 m = 1,000 N m
(small moment)

2 m
500 N

moment = force × distance
= 1,000 N × 4 m = 4,000 N m
(large moment)

4 m
1,000 N

Balancing moments

To investigate the law of the lever

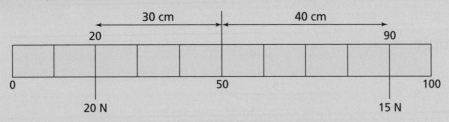

Procedure

1. Hang a metre stick from a stand.
2. Adjust the metre stick until it is balanced. It is at its centre of gravity.
3. Hang the two weights on the metre stick until the lever is balanced.
4. Calculate the moments on the left-hand and the right-hand side by multiplying the force by the perpendicular distance in each case.

Results

moments on left = moments on right

$20 \text{ N} \times 30 \text{ cm} = 15 \text{ N} \times 40 \text{ cm}$

$20 \text{ N} \times 0.3 \text{ m} = 15 \text{ N} \times 0.4 \text{ m}$

$6 \text{ N m} = 6 \text{ N m}$

Conclusion

When an object is balanced, the moments on the left equal the moments on the right.

Levers at equilibrium

Law of the lever: When a lever is balanced, the sum of the moments on the left equals the sum of the moments on the right.

Example

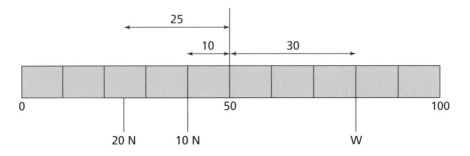

The lever in the diagram is balanced under the action of the forces shown. Find the value of W.

moments on left = moments on right

$(20 \times 25) + (10 \times 10) = W \times 30$

$500 + 100 = 30 \times W$

$600 = 30\,W$

$W = 20\,N$

Centre of gravity

In the previous diagram, the metre stick was suspended at the midpoint. This point is where the **weight appears to act**.

> The **centre of gravity** of an object is the point where all its weight appears to act.

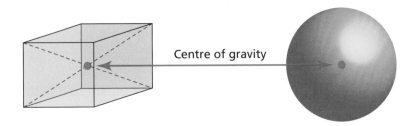

Centre of gravity

exam focus

HL

To find the centre of gravity of a sheet of cardboard (a thin lamina)

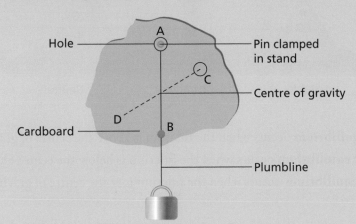

Hole

Pin clamped in stand

Centre of gravity

Cardboard

Plumbline

A, B, C, D

Procedure

1. Hang the cardboard from a pin on a stand. Make sure that it is free to swing.
2. When the cardboard comes to rest, draw a vertical line on the cardboard along the plumb line.
3. Hang the cardboard from a different position. Repeat step 2.
4. The centre of gravity is the point where the two lines cross.

Stability

When buildings are designed, great care is taken to ensure that they do not topple over, i.e. that they are in stable equilibrium. This is done by making sure that each building has a wide base and that the centre of gravity is as low as possible.

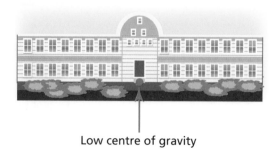

Low centre of gravity

Stable, unstable and neutral equilibrium

CG = centre of gravity, fulcrum at X

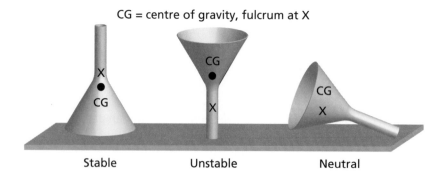

Stable   Unstable   Neutral

- **Stable equilibrium** occurs when the fulcrum is above the centre of gravity.
- **Unstable equilibrium** occurs when the fulcrum is below the centre of gravity.
- **Neutral equilibrium** occurs when the fulcrum is at the centre of gravity.

Sample questions and answers

1. *In an experiment, a student measured the increase in length of a spiral spring caused by adding a series of weights to the spring. The weights were added until the spring was damaged. The data from the experiment is given in the table below. Plot a graph of extension against weight. (Junior Cert 2006, Q9a)*

Weight (N)	0.0	0.4	0.8	1.2	1.6	2.0	2.4
Extension (cm)	0.0	2.0	4.0	6.0	8.0	8.5	8.6

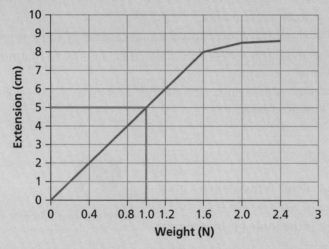

(a) *Use the graph to estimate the weight that would produce an extension of 5 cm in the spring.*

Answer

Weight = 1.0 N at extension of 5 cm.

(b) *From the graph, estimate the weight that causes damage to the spring where Hooke's law no longer applies.*

Answer

Weights = greater than 1.6 N.

2. *A metre stick is suspended from its centre of gravity at 50 cm. A force of 3.5 N is suspended at the 90 cm mark and an unknown force acts on the stick at the 30 cm mark. The metre stick is balanced. Calculate the value of the unknown force F.*

Answer

moment on left-hand side = moment on right-hand side

$$20 \text{ cm} \times F = 40 \text{ cm} \times 3.5 \text{ N}$$

$$F = \frac{40 \text{ cm} \times 3.5 \text{ N}}{20 \text{ cm}} = 7 \text{ N}$$

26 Work, Power and Energy

aims **In this chapter you need to learn:**

1. The definitions of work, power and energy.
2. How to do calculations on work and power.
3. The different types of energy and how energy is converted into other forms of energy.
4. The law of conservation of energy.
5. Mandatory experiments:
   (a) To show the conversion of chemical energy to heat energy.
   (b) To show the conversion of electrical energy to magnetic energy to kinetic energy.
   (c) To show the conversion of light energy to electrical energy to kinetic energy.

Work

Work is done and energy is used when a body is moved.

The unit of work is the joule (J) or newton metre, N m.

1 joule of work is done when a force of 1 newton moves a body 1 metre.

key point

work done = force × distance moved

HL Example

What is the work done when a 30 N brick is lifted through a vertical height of 2 metres?

work done = force × distance moved

work done = 30 N × 2 m = 60 N m = 60 J

2 m

30 N

Power

Power is measured in **watts (W)**.

key point

Power is the amount of work done per second.

key point

1 watt = 1 joule per second (J s^{-1})

Example

A man pushes a supermarket trolley with a force of 30 N for a distance of 200 m from the door of the supermarket to his car. If the journey took 150 seconds, calculate his average power.

$$\text{work} = \text{force} \times \text{distance}$$
$$= 30 \text{ N} \times 200 \text{ m}$$
$$= 6{,}000 \text{ N m}$$
$$= 6{,}000 \text{ J}$$

$$\text{power} = \frac{\text{work}}{\text{time}} = \frac{6{,}000 \text{ J}}{150 \text{ s}} = 40 \text{ J s}^{-1} = 40 \text{ W}$$

Energy

When something has energy, it is capable of doing work.

Different types of energy

key point

Energy is the ability to do work. It is measured in joules (J).

- **Kinetic energy** is the energy an object has when it is moving.

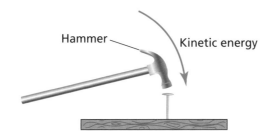

Hammer — Kinetic energy

- **Potential energy** is stored energy waiting to do work.

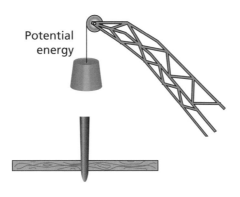

Potential energy

- **Chemical energy** is stored energy in oil, gas, coal and all other chemicals, waiting to react.
- **Nuclear energy** is stored energy in radioactive substances. It is used in power stations to make electricity.
- **Electrical energy** is one of the most useful forms of energy. It can be used in many forms, including heat, light and sound.
- **Heat energy** is in all objects at a temperature above zero Kelvin. The heat energy is generated because of particle movement – the greater the movement, the greater the heat energy released.
- **Light energy** travels in waves. The energy from the sun takes the form of light and heat energy.
- **Sound energy** travels in waves. Sound causes our eardrums to vibrate, enabling us to distinguish different sounds.

The sun is the primary source of all energy.

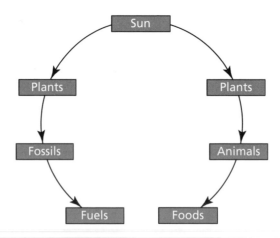

Energy source	Advantages	Disadvantages
Fossil fuel	Cheap. Can be stored.	Limited supply. Non-renewable. Pollutes the atmosphere.
Solar	Free, unlimited supply. No pollution.	Difficult to store. Costly.
Wind	Free, unlimited supply. No pollution.	Wind is unreliable. Unsightly.
Tidal	Free, unlimited supply. No pollution.	Variable supply. Unsightly.
Nuclear	Large supply from small fuel source. No atmospheric pollution.	Non-renewable. Produces radioactive waste. Possible nuclear accidents.

Mandatory experiment

(a) To show the conversion of chemical energy to heat energy

key point

The **law of conservation of energy** states that energy cannot be created or destroyed, but can only be changed from one form into another.

Procedure

1. Set up the electrical circuit as shown.
2. Close the switch.

Result

The bulb lights. The filament inside the bulb gets hot.

Conclusion

The chemical energy in the battery is converted to electrical energy. The bulb then converts the electrical energy to heat energy.

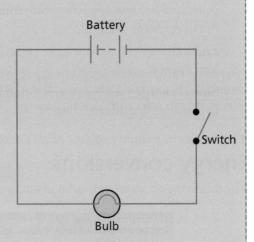

Battery

Switch

Bulb

(b) To show the conversion of electrical energy to magnetic energy to kinetic energy

Procedure

1. Set up the electrical circuit as shown.
2. Close the switch.

Result

When the current is switched on, the nail becomes magnetised and attracts the pins. When the current is switched off, the nail loses its magnetism.

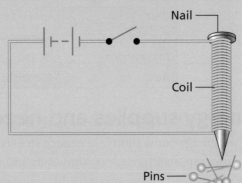

Nail

Coil

Pins

Conclusion

The electrical energy in the wire is converted to magnetic energy in the nail. The magnetic energy in the nail is converted to kinetic energy in the pins.

(c) To show the conversion of light energy to electrical energy to kinetic energy

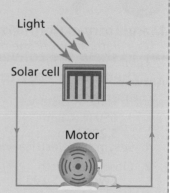

Procedure

1. Set up the electrical circuit as shown.
2. Shine a bright light on the solar cell.

Result

The electric motor spins.

Conclusion

The solar cell converts light energy to electrical energy. The electrical energy in the motor enables the motor to spin with kinetic energy.

Energy conversions

The following are some examples of energy conversions.

Instrument	Energy in	Energy out
Coiled spring	Potential	Kinetic
Generator	Kinetic	Electrical
Motor	Electrical	Kinetic
Battery	Chemical	Electrical
Car	Chemical	Kinetic
Microphone	Sound	Electrical
Bulb	Electrical	Light

Energy supplies and needs

Many energy conversions are needed in everyday life, e.g. in cooking, heating and for electrical appliances such as computers and television sets.

Energy comes from **non-renewable sources** like coal, gas and other fossil fuels. This energy may be used up someday.

Energy also comes from **renewable sources** such as solar energy, wind energy, wave energy, geothermal energy and hydroelectric energy.

Saving energy

Energy can be saved by:

- Better insulation of houses and factories.
- Increasing the efficiency of machines.
- Reusing and recycling materials.

Sample questions and answers

1. *A girl of mass 65 kg (650 N) climbed stairs that were 8 m high in 20 seconds. Calculate the work she did and the average power she developed while climbing the stairs.*

Answer

work = force × distance

= 650 N × 8 m

= 5,200 N m

= 5,200 J

$$\text{power} = \frac{\text{work}}{\text{time}} = \frac{5,200 \text{ J}}{20 \text{ s}} = 260 \text{ J s}^{-1} = 260 \text{ W}$$

2. *Using a labelled diagram, describe how chemical energy is converted to electrical energy.*

Answer

  (i) Set up the circuit as shown in the diagram.

  (ii) Close the switch.

Result: The bulb lights. The filament inside the bulb gets hot.

Conclusion: The chemical energy in the battery is converted to electrical energy. The bulb converts the electrical energy into heat energy.

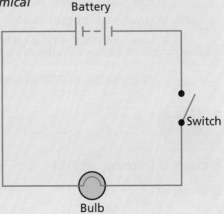

27 Pressure

key point

Pressure is force per unit area.

$$\text{pressure} = \frac{\text{force}}{\text{area}}$$

The effect of a force on a substance depends on how it is spread out over its surface.

The two women in the diagram have the **same weight**. The woman with the stiletto heels can cause damage to the floor covering because her weight is concentrated over a small area. Because her weight is spread over a small area it produces high pressure, while the weight of the other woman, which is spread over a large area, is producing low pressure.

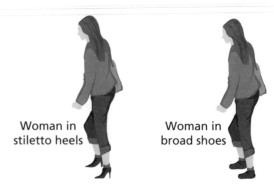

Woman in stiletto heels   Woman in broad shoes

Pressure is measured in **pascals**, where **1 pascal (Pa) = 1 N/m².**

Example

A block with the dimensions 2 m × 3 m × 4 m can rest on three different surfaces, A, B and C. If the weight of the block is 600 N, find the smallest pressure it can exert on the surface.

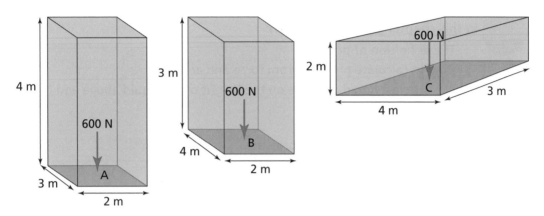

Surface A

area of surface A = 3 m × 2 m = 6 m²

$$\text{pressure} = \frac{\text{force}}{\text{area}} = \frac{600\text{ N}}{6\text{ m}^2} = 100\text{ N/m}^2 \text{ (or } 100\text{ N m}^{-2})$$

Surface B

area of surface B = 4 m × 2 m = 8 m²

$$\text{pressure} = \frac{\text{force}}{\text{area}} = \frac{600\text{ N}}{8\text{ m}^2} = 75\text{ N/m}^2 \text{ (or } 75\text{ N m}^{-2})$$

Surface C

area of surface C = 3 m × 4 m = 12 m²

$$\text{pressure} = \frac{\text{force}}{\text{area}} = \frac{600\text{ N}}{12\text{ m}^2} = 50\text{ N/m}^2 \text{ (or } 50\text{ N m}^{-2})$$

Therefore, the smallest pressure is exerted by surface C.

Pressure in fluids (liquids and gases)

When underwater, a diver experiences pressure from the liquid all around him. The deeper he dives, the greater is the pressure exerted.

The **pressure in a liquid** depends on the height of the liquid above and on the density of the liquid.

1. Pressure increases with depth.
2. Width or shape do not affect pressure.
3. Pressure in a liquid is the same in all directions.

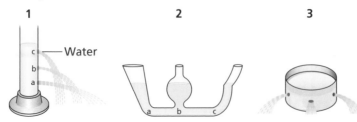

Atmospheric pressure

Air is a fluid and exerts pressure in the same way that water does.

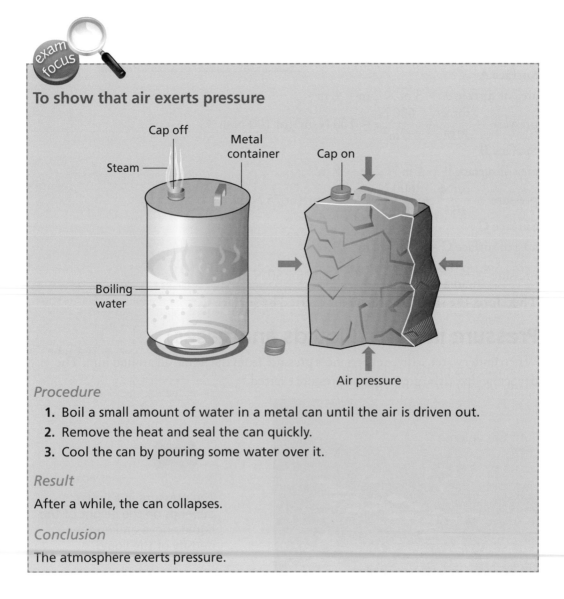

exam focus

To show that air exerts pressure

Procedure

1. Boil a small amount of water in a metal can until the air is driven out.
2. Remove the heat and seal the can quickly.
3. Cool the can by pouring some water over it.

Result

After a while, the can collapses.

Conclusion

The atmosphere exerts pressure.

To show that air has mass

Procedure

1. Find the mass of a deflated football using a balance.
2. Pump air into the football.
3. Find the mass of the pumped-up football.

Result

The pumped-up football is heavier.

Conclusion

Air has mass.

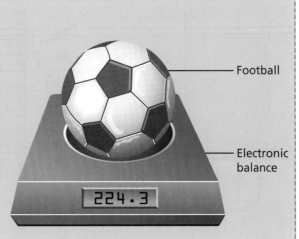

Football

Electronic balance

224.3

To show that air has volume

Procedure

1. Set up the apparatus as shown in the diagram.
2. Blow some air into the test tube.

Result

The water is pushed out of the test tube by the air blown in.

Conclusion

Air has volume.

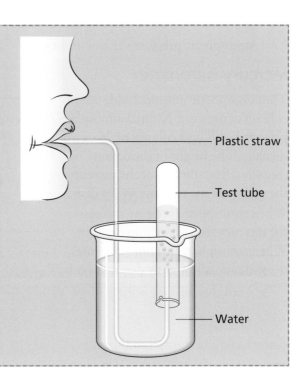

Plastic straw

Test tube

Water

Other effects of atmospheric pressure

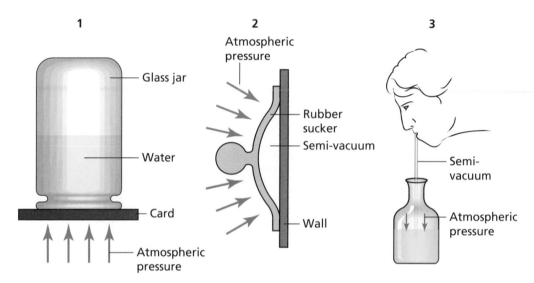

1. Atmospheric pressure holds the card in place.
2. Rubber suckers are held on by atmospheric pressure.
3. When the air is sucked out, atmospheric pressure pushes the liquid up.

Measuring atmospheric pressure

- An instrument called a **barometer** is used to measure atmospheric pressure.
- Atmospheric pressure varies with height.

Mercury barometer

The atmospheric pressure holds up the column of mercury. Normal atmospheric pressure holds up a column of 76 cm of mercury. The height of the column is measured from the top of the mercury to the surface of the mercury in the dish.

When atmospheric pressure increases, the mercury rises slightly up the tube. When atmospheric pressure decreases, the mercury falls slightly down the tube.

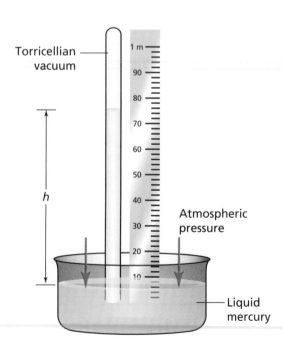

The aneroid barometer (no liquid)

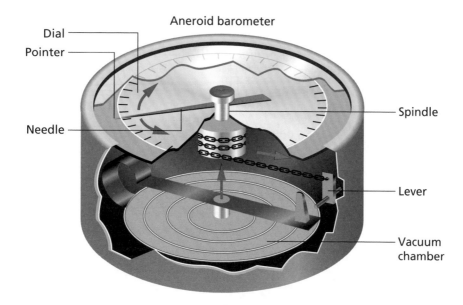

Aneroid barometer

Dial

Pointer

Needle

Spindle

Lever

Vacuum chamber

An **aneroid barometer** is made of a partially evacuated corrugated box. If atmospheric pressure increases, the box is crushed slightly, causing the pointer to move. When the pressure decreases, the pointer moves the other way.

Altitude and pressure

When we move higher above sea level, the atmospheric pressure decreases. An instrument called an **altimeter** is used by pilots to measure height above sea level. It does this by measuring the pressure on a barometer.

Weather and pressure

When the atmospheric pressure is **high**, water vapour does not rise from the ground. This means that rain clouds do not form and the weather is fine and sunny.

When the atmospheric pressure is **low**, water vapour rises up from the ground. Rain clouds form, which may cause rain.

Weather charts and isobars

The lines on a weather chart show areas of equal pressure. These lines are called **isobars**. These isobars are shown on weather charts as areas of high pressure and low pressure.

Sample questions and answers

1. *A cubic box 500 cm long and weighing 1,500 N rests on a surface. Calculate the pressure exerted by the box on the surface.*

Answer

area of surface of box = 500 cm × 500 cm = 0.5 m × 0.5 m = 0.25 m²

$$pressure = \frac{force}{area} = \frac{1{,}500\ N}{0.25\ m^2} = 6{,}000\ N\ m^{-2}$$

2. *How does an aneroid barometer work?*

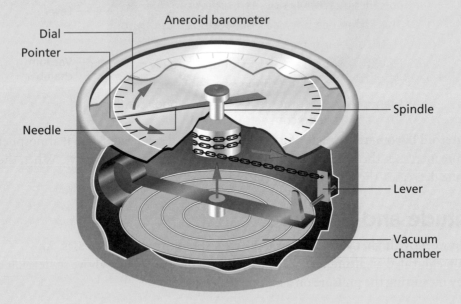

Aneroid barometer

Dial

Pointer

Needle

Spindle

Lever

Vacuum chamber

Answer

   (i)   An aneroid barometer is made of a partially evacuated corrugated box.

  (ii) As atmospheric pressure increases, the box is squeezed slightly, causing the pointer to move.

 (iii) As atmospheric pressure decreases, the box expands slightly, causing the pointer to move the other way.

28 Heat and Temperature

In this chapter you need to learn:

1. The definition of heat.
2. Expansion and contraction of solids, liquids and gases.
3. Mandatory experiment: To investigate the expansion and contraction of solids, liquids and gases.
4. Mandatory experiment: To show the transfer of heat energy by conduction, convection and radiation.
5. The difference between heat and temperature.
6. How to demonstrate changes of state.
7. How to examine the effect of pressure on the boiling point of water.
8. How to examine the shape of a cooling curve.
9. Mandatory experiments: (a) Water is poor conductor of heat and (b) water is good convector of heat.
10. How to compare insulators.

Heat as energy

Heat is a form of energy. It is measured in **joules (J)**. It can cause movement of particles and can be converted into other forms of energy.

Expansion and contraction

- Solids, liquids and gases expand when they are heated and contract when they are cooled.
- Substances expand when they are heated because the particles vibrate more quickly and take up more space.
- Gases expand more than liquids, while liquids expand more than solids.

Mandatory experiment

(a) To investigate the expansion and contraction of solids

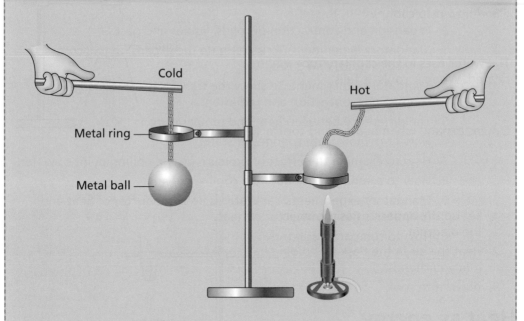

Procedure

1. Check that the cold ball slips through the ring.
2. Heat the ball strongly.
3. Allow it to cool.

Result

The ball will not fit through the ring when heated. When it cools, it slips through the ring.

Conclusion

Solids expand when heated and contract when cooled.

(b) To investigate the expansion and contraction of liquids

Procedure

1. Mark the level of the liquid in the capillary tube.
2. Heat the liquid in the flask.
3. Allow it to cool.

Result

The water rises in the capillary tube when heated. When it cools, it falls.

Conclusion

Liquids expand when heated and contract when cooled.

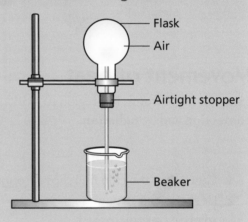

Level rises

Liquid

(c) To investigate the expansion and contraction of gases

Procedure

1. Set up the apparatus as shown in the diagram.
2. Heat the air in the flask by holding it in your hands.
3. Allow it to cool.

Result

Air bubbles rise in the beaker of water.

Conclusion

Gases expand when heated and contract when cooled.

Flask

Air

Airtight stopper

Beaker

Water is an unusual substance. When water is cooled down to 4°C, it contracts. If it cools below 4°C, it begins to expand. This means that ice floats on water. This is important because it allows animals and plants to survive under the ice in winter.

key point

Ice expands when cooled below 4°C.

Demonstration of the expansion of water upon freezing

Procedure

1. Place a glass bottle full of water into a plastic bag.
2. Place it in a freezer overnight.

Result

The glass bottle bursts.

Conclusion

The water expanded upon freezing and burst the bottle.

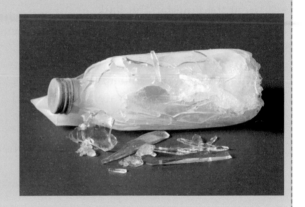

Movement of heat

Heat can move from a hot region to a cold region in three ways: by **conduction**, by **convection** and by **radiation**.

Mandatory experiment

(a) To show the transfer of heat energy by conduction

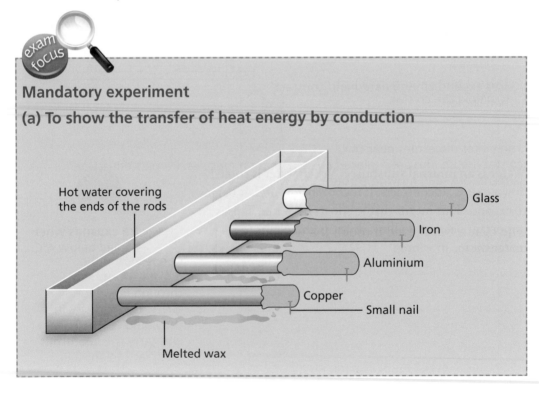

Hot water covering the ends of the rods

Glass

Iron

Aluminium

Copper

Small nail

Melted wax

Procedure

1. Set up the apparatus as shown in the diagram.
2. Pour boiling water into the container.

Results

The wax begins to melt. The small nail under the wax will fall from the copper first, then the other nails fall off in stages. Some substances are better conductors of heat than others.

Conclusion

The heat contained in the water has travelled along the rods by conduction.

Conduction is the movement of heat through a substance without the substance moving.

(b) To show the transfer of heat energy by convection

Procedure

1. Place some cold water in a beaker.
2. Drop a crystal of potassium permanganate down a funnel into a corner of the beaker.
3. Heat the water gently just below the crystal.

— Purple streaks

— Clear water

— Potassium permanganate

— Small flame

Results

The water molecules near the crystal rise up and are replaced by cold water molecules. Purple convection currents are seen moving through the water.

Conclusion

The heat is transferred through the water by convection.

Convection is the movement of heat through liquids and gases. The particles in the liquid or gas move and carry the heat from one place to another.

(c) To show the transfer of heat energy by radiation

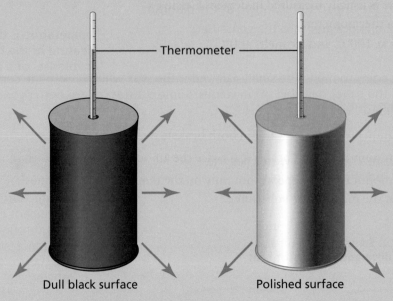

Thermometer

Dull black surface   Polished surface

Procedure

1. Find two cans of equal size: one polished and shiny, the other dull and black.
2. Put a thermometer in each can and fill each can with equal amounts of boiling water.
3. Cover each can. Record the temperature every 2 minutes.

Result

The temperature falls faster in the darker can.

Conclusion

The heat is radiated from the hot cans. Black surfaces are better radiators of heat than bright surfaces.

Radiation is the transfer of heat, in rays, from a hot body without needing a medium to travel through. Radiation travels in straight lines at the speed of light.

Temperature

Temperature is usually measured in degrees Celsius (°C) using a thermometer.

Water boils at 100°C and ice melts at 0°C.

Temperature is the measure of the hotness or coldness of a body.

Heat and temperature

- The temperature of the water in both beakers is the same.
- The amount of heat in beaker 2 is twice the amount of that in beaker 1.
- The amount of heat depends not only on the temperature of the substance, but also on the **mass of the substance**.

Same temperatures, different amounts of heat

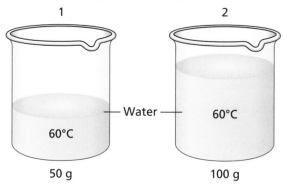

- The temperature of the liquids in both beakers is the same.
- The amount of heat in beaker 2 is different to that in beaker 1.
- The amount of heat also depends on the **nature of the substance**.

Same temperatures, same mass, different amounts of heat

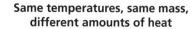

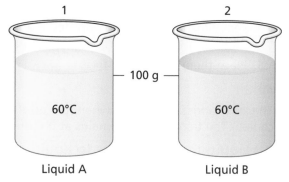

Heat depends on temperature, mass and the nature of the substance.

Changes of state

- **Melting and freezing:** When ice receives heat energy, it melts. It changes from a solid to a liquid. When water loses heat, it freezes and changes into ice.
- **Evaporation and boiling:** When water is heated, it evaporates and changes into steam. It changes from a liquid into a gas. Evaporation occurs at the surface of the liquid. When it occurs throughout the liquid, the liquid is at its boiling point. When steam loses heat energy, it condenses and changes into water.

$$\text{solid} \iff \text{liquid} \iff \text{gas}$$
$$\text{ice} \iff \text{water} \iff \text{steam}$$

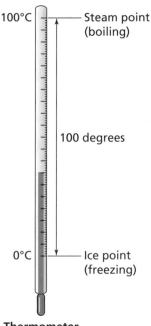

100°C — Steam point (boiling)

100 degrees

0°C — Ice point (freezing)

Thermometer

There is no change in temperature during a change of state.

To show changes of state

(a) Solid to liquid and liquid to solid

Procedure
1. Place some ice cubes in a beaker.
2. Measure the temperature of the ice cubes with a thermometer.
3. Leave them aside for 20 minutes in a warm spot.
4. Measure the temperature again before they have fully melted.
5. Place them back in the freezer.

Result
The ice changes into water when heated. The water changes back into ice when cooled. The temperature remains at 0°C during the change of state.

(b) Liquid to gas and gas to liquid

Procedure
1. Heat some water in a beaker until it boils.
2. Measure the temperature of the water.
3. Allow the steam to hit a cold surface.

Result
The water changes into steam when heated. The steam changes back into water when cooled. The temperature remains at 100°C during the change of state.

To investigate the effect of pressure on the boiling point of water

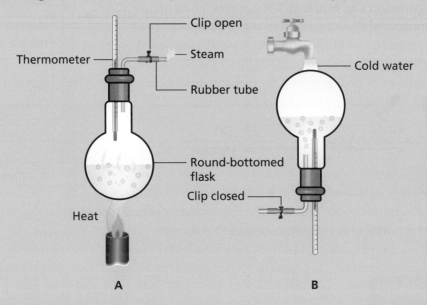

Procedure

1. With the clip open, boil some water in the round-bottomed flask.
2. Note the temperature of the water.
3. Remove the heat.
4. Close the clip on the tubing and cool the flask by pouring some cold water on it.
5. Measure the temperature again.

Result

The water boils on cooling at a temperature lower than 100°C.

Conclusion

At reduced pressure, the water boils at a lower temperature.

Cooling curves and latent heat

The heat taken in during melting and boiling is called **latent heat**.

To plot a cooling curve

Procedure

1. Gently heat some butter in a test tube until it melts.
2. As the butter cools, measure its temperature every 30 seconds.
3. Plot a graph of temperature against time.

Results

Temperature (°C)	60	50	40	31	31	31	31	31	31	31	31	25	20
Time (minutes)	0.5	1.0	1.5	2.0	2.5	3.0	3.5	4.0	4.5	5.0	5.5	6.0	6.5

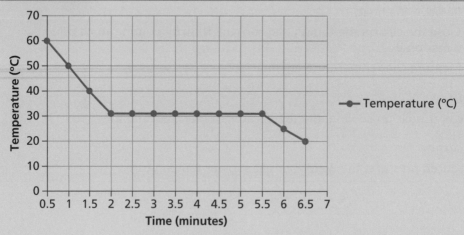

Conclusion

When the liquid butter is changing state into a solid, **the temperature does not change**. The butter is losing heat – this heat is called **latent (hidden) heat**.

Mandatory experiment

(a) Water is a poor conductor of heat

Procedure

Heat the water at the top of the test tube.

Result

The water at the top boils. The ice at the bottom does not melt.

Conclusion

This shows that water is a poor conductor of heat.

Water boiling

Poor conduction through water

Wire to keep ice at bottom

Unmelted ice

(b) Water is a good convector of heat

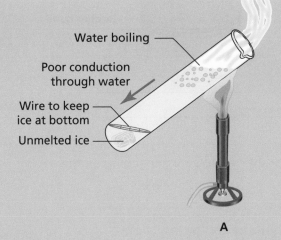

Water boiling

Poor conduction through water

Wire to keep ice at bottom

Unmelted ice

A

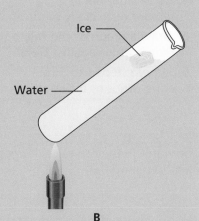

Ice

Water

B

Procedure

1. Heat the water at the top of test tube A.
2. Heat the water at the bottom of test tube B.

Results

1. The water at the top of A boils. The ice at the bottom does not melt.
2. The ice at the top of B melts.

Conclusion

This shows that water is a good convector of heat.

Insulation

- Non-metals (such as wood, wool and glass), liquids and gases are good insulators (or are bad conductors).
- The insulating ability of a material is given by its **tog value**. The higher the tog value, the better the insulator.

An **insulator** is a substance that does not allow heat to move through it easily.

exam focus

To compare the insulating ability of different materials

Procedure

1. Fill a metal can with boiling water.
2. Measure the temperature of the water.
3. Wrap the can in the material to be tested.
4. Record the fall in temperature every minute.
5. Draw a graph of the fall in temperature against time.
6. Repeat steps 1 to 5 for equal strips of different materials.

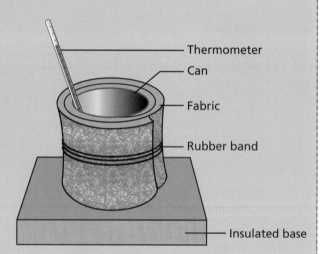

Thermometer

Can

Fabric

Rubber band

Insulated base

Result

The water in the can takes longer (or shorter) to cool depending on the particular material.

Conclusion

The slower the drop in temperature, the better the insulator.

Sample questions and answers

1. *Describe an experiment to show the expansion of water as it freezes. (Junior Cert 2006, Q8b)*

Answer

  (i) Place a glass bottle full of water into a plastic bag.

  (ii) Place it in a freezer overnight.

Result: The glass bottle bursts.

Conclusion: The water expanded upon freezing and burst the bottle.

2. *A student heated some naphthalene in a test tube until it melted. As the naphthalene cooled, the temperature of the napthalene was taken every minute. The data is given in the table below. (Junior Cert 2006, Q8c)*

Temperature (°C)	105	100	95	90	85	80	80	80	80	80	80	75	70	65	60
Time (minutes)	0	1	2	3	4	5	6	7	8	9	10	11	12	13	14

  (a) *Plot a graph of the cooling curve.*

    Answer

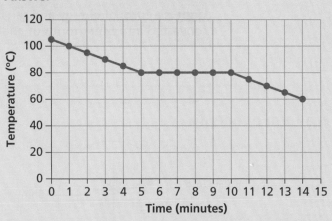

  (b) *What is happening to the naphthalene between 5 minutes and 10 minutes?*

    Answer

    It is changing state – from a liquid into a solid.

  (c) *What is this heat loss between 5 minutes and 10 minutes called?*

    Answer

    Latent heat.

29 Light

aims **In this chapter you need to learn:**

1. Light is a form of energy.
2. Mandatory experiments:
   (a) To show that light travels in straight lines.
   (b) To explain how shadows are formed.
3. Mandatory experiment: To investigate the reflection of light by plane mirrors.
4. Mandatory experiment: To demonstrate the operation of a periscope.
5. To show refraction of light.
6. The different types of lenses.
7. Refraction of light through a lens.

Light

key point

Light is a form of energy and can be converted into other forms of energy.

exam focus

To show that light is a form of energy

Procedure
Shine a bright light on the radiometer.

Result
The vanes on the radiometer move.

Conclusion
Light energy is converted into kinetic energy.

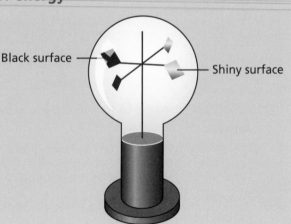

Black surface — Shiny surface

Mandatory experiment

(a) To show that light travels in straight lines

Procedure

1. Place three identical cards with a small hole in each about 10 cm apart.
2. Arrange them so that the holes are in a straight line.
3. Look through the holes to see the light.
4. Move one of the cards slightly to one side.

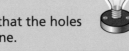

Result

The light can only be seen when the cards are in a straight line.

Conclusion

Light travels in straight lines.

(b) To explain how shadows are formed

Procedure

1. Arrange the light, your hand and the screen as shown.
2. Note the shadow formed on the screen.
3. Move your hand closer to the screen. Move it away from the screen.

Results

1. The shadow is the same shape as your hand.
2. The shadow is large when it is close to the light and small when it is far from the light.

Conclusion

Shadows are formed when light cannot pass through an object – such substances are said to be **opaque**. Shadows show that light travels in straight lines.

Luminous and non-luminous objects

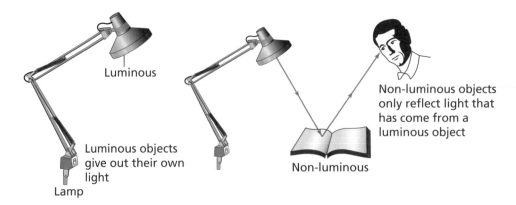

Luminous

Luminous objects give out their own light

Lamp

Non-luminous

Non-luminous objects only reflect light that has come from a luminous object

exam focus

Mandatory experiment

To investigate the reflection of light by plane mirrors

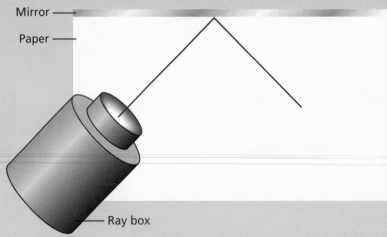

Mirror

Paper

Ray box

Procedure

1. Place a ray box on a piece of white paper opposite a plane mirror.
2. Draw a line on the paper along the path of the ray going towards the mirror.
3. Draw a line on the paper along the ray coming back from the mirror.
4. Move the mirror at different angles to the ray box. Repeat steps 2 and 3.

Result

The rays of light are reflected from the mirror in straight lines in a regular pattern.

Conclusion

Light is reflected from the surface of a plane mirror in a regular pattern.

Mandatory experiment

To demonstrate the operation of a periscope

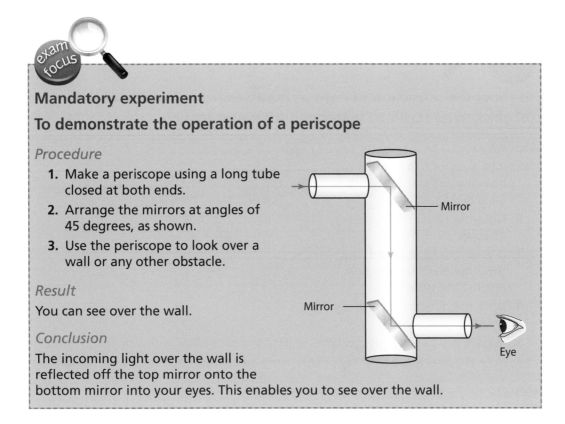

Procedure

1. Make a periscope using a long tube closed at both ends.
2. Arrange the mirrors at angles of 45 degrees, as shown.
3. Use the periscope to look over a wall or any other obstacle.

Result

You can see over the wall.

Conclusion

The incoming light over the wall is reflected off the top mirror onto the bottom mirror into your eyes. This enables you to see over the wall.

Refraction of light

> **key point**
>
> **Refraction** is the bending of light when it travels from one transparent substance to another.

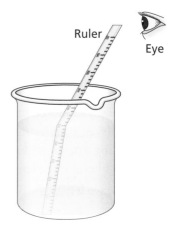

Light is bent when rays of light pass from one medium to another.

The ruler seems to be broken when it is placed at an angle in the water. This shows that the light rays are bent as they emerge from the water.

To show the refraction of light as it passes from (a) air to glass (b) glass to air (c) air to water and (d) water to air

Procedure

1. Pass a ray of light from a ray box through the air into a glass block, as shown.

2. Note the direction of the ray of light.

3. Repeat the experiment, but this time place the ray box against the glass block.

4. Note the direction of the ray of light.

5. Repeat steps 1 to 4, but this time, replace the glass block with a beaker of water.

6. Note the direction of the ray of light from air to water and from water to air.

Ray box

Sheet of paper

Glass block

Results

The rays of light are bent when moving from one medium to another.

Conclusion

Light is refracted when it enters another transparent medium.

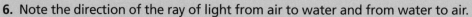

Lenses

key point

- **Convex lenses** are converging lenses (they come together). They are thicker at the middle than at the edges. If you look at something through a convex lens, it looks bigger. Convex lenses are used in magnifying glasses, microscopes, spectacles and contact lenses.

A **lens** is a piece of glass or other transparent material that has a curved surface.

- A **magnifying glass** is a convex lens that uses refraction to give an enlarged view of an object. The lens is usually mounted in a frame with a handle. A magnifying glass works by creating a magnified image of an object behind the lens.

- **Concave lenses** are diverging lenses (they spread out). They are thinner at the middle than at the edges.

To show refraction of light through a lens

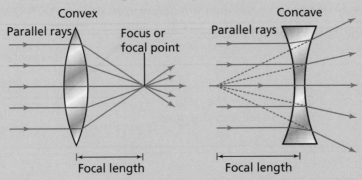

Procedure

1. In a darkened room, shine a number of parallel rays from a ray box through a convex lens.

2. Observe what happens.

3. Repeat steps 1 and 2 using a concave lens.

Results

For the convex lens, the rays converge (come together).
For the concave lens, the rays diverge (spread out).

To show that white light is separated by dispersion

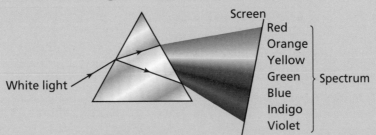

Procedure

Use a ray box to shine a ray of white light through a triangular prism.

Result

When a ray of white light enters the prism, it is bent and emerges as a band of colours called a spectrum.

Conclusion

White light is made up of different colours.

Sample questions and answers

1. *The path of a light ray entering from the air into a glass block and then exiting into the air again is shown in the diagram below. (Junior Cert 2007, Q9a)*

   (a) *What is the bending of light called?*

   Answer

   Refraction.

   (b) *From the rays P, Q, R or S, pick the path taken by the light ray on leaving the glass.*

   Answer

   S

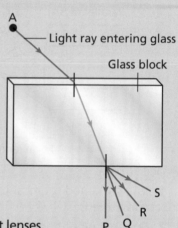

A

Light ray entering glass

Glass block

P   Q   R   S

   (c) *Give an application of this bending of light.*

   Answer

   Convex lenses in spectacles and contact lenses.

   Concave lenses in cameras, spectacles and contact lenses.

   (d) *Name another way in which the direction of light can be changed.*

   Answer

   By reflection.

30 Sound

In this chapter you need to learn:

1. Sound is a form of energy produced by vibrations.
2. Sound cannot travel through a vacuum.
3. Sound can be reflected.
4. Light travels faster than sound.
5. Hearing is caused by sound vibrations on the eardrum.

Sound

exam focus

To show that sound is form of energy and is produced by vibrations

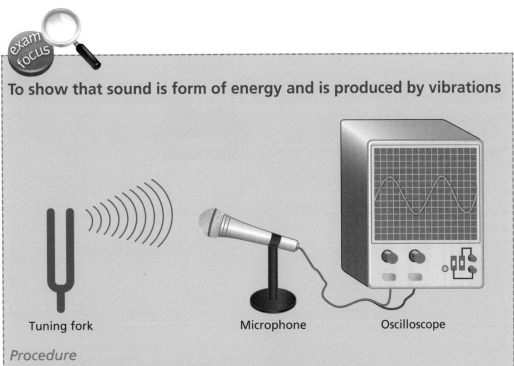

Tuning fork   Microphone   Oscilloscope

Procedure

1. Hold a vibrating tuning fork in front of the microphone.
2. Observe the wave pattern on the oscilloscope.
3. Stop the tuning fork vibrating by holding it tightly in your hand.
4. Observe what happens to the pattern on the oscilloscope.

Results

A wave pattern appears on the oscilloscope when the tuning fork is vibrating. It does not appear when the tuning fork does not vibrate.

Conclusions

1. The sound from the tuning fork is converted into electrical energy by the microphone. Sound is a form of energy.
2. Sound is produced by vibrations.
3. A wave pattern appears on the oscilloscope screen.

Sound cannot travel through a vacuum – it requires a medium

Procedure

1. Allow the bell to ring.
2. Slowly evacuate the air from the jar.

Result

The sound begins to fade. When all the air is evacuated, no sound is heard, even though the hammer is still striking the gong.

Conclusion

Sound transmission requires a medium.

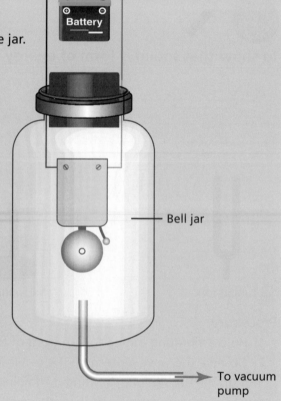

Bell jar

To vacuum pump

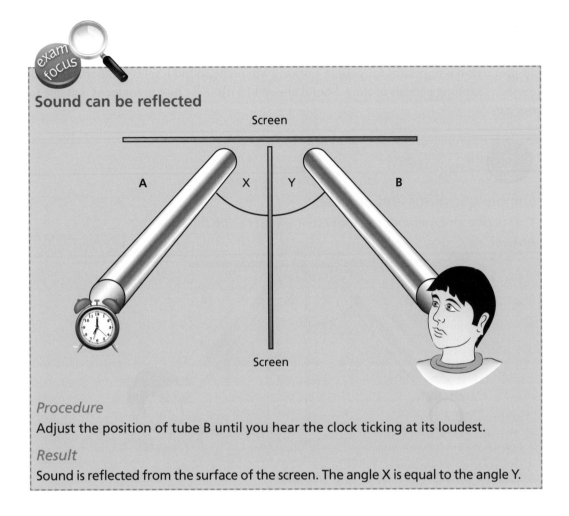

exam
focus

Sound can be reflected

Procedure
Adjust the position of tube B until you hear the clock ticking at its loudest.

Result
Sound is reflected from the surface of the screen. The angle X is equal to the angle Y.

- **Echoes** are sounds that are reflected from a surface.
- **Ultrasound** is sound of a very high pitch. The sound vibrates very quickly – humans cannot hear it. It is used to 'see' body organs such as the heart, tumours, unborn babies and other objects.

Speed of sound in air

Sound travels through air at 330 m s^{-1}. Light travels much faster than sound. It travels at 300,000,000 m s^{-1}, nearly a million times faster than sound.

The huge difference in the speeds of light and sound means that **you see something before you hear it.** The most common example of this is thunder and lightning.

Hearing sounds

Sound is produced by vibrations. These vibrations cause the air to vibrate. The vibrating air particles are directed by the outer ear onto the eardrum. The vibrations on the eardrum are converted into electrical energy and are transmitted to the brain. The brain converts the electrical energy into familiar sounds.

Noise protection

Loud sounds are high in energy – strong vibrations can cause damage to your eardrums. Ear protection is necessary for people working where the sound level is more than 70 dB (decibels) for long periods of time. Sound above 115 dB will cause permanent damage to your ears.

exam
Q

Sample questions and answers

1. *Describe an experiment to show that sound can be reflected.*
Answer

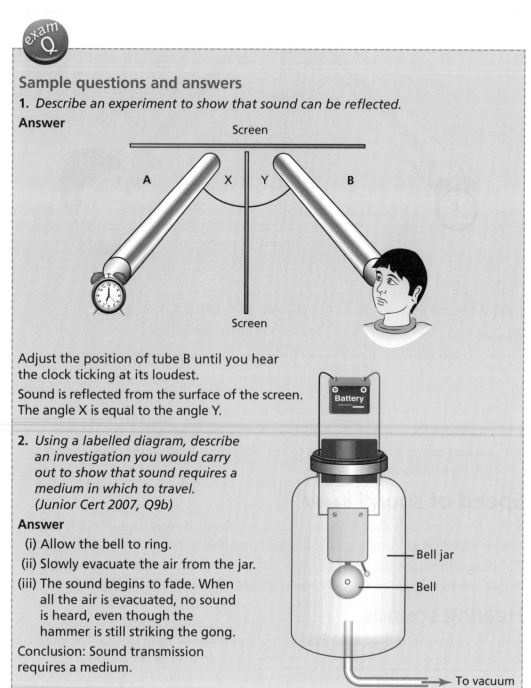

Adjust the position of tube B until you hear the clock ticking at its loudest.

Sound is reflected from the surface of the screen. The angle X is equal to the angle Y.

2. *Using a labelled diagram, describe an investigation you would carry out to show that sound requires a medium in which to travel. (Junior Cert 2007, Q9b)*

Answer

 (i) Allow the bell to ring.

 (ii) Slowly evacuate the air from the jar.

(iii) The sound begins to fade. When all the air is evacuated, no sound is heard, even though the hammer is still striking the gong.

Conclusion: Sound transmission requires a medium.

In this chapter you need to learn:

1. How to show attraction and repulsion between magnets.
2. Mandatory experiment: To plot the magnetic field of a bar magnet.
3. The earth's magnetic poles are not exactly the same as the geographical poles.

Magnetism

Substances that can be magnetised are **iron, steel, nickel and cobalt**.

To show attraction and repulsion between magnets

Procedure

1. Suspend a bar magnet from a wooden stand.
2. Bring the north pole of another magnet close to the north pole of the suspended magnet.
3. Bring the south pole close to the north pole.
4. Bring the south pole close to the south pole.
5. Note what happens.

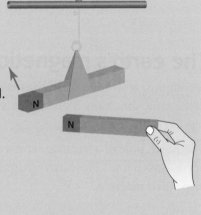

Results

The north poles repel each other. The south poles repel each other. The north and south poles attract each other.

Conclusion

Like poles repel, unlike poles attract.

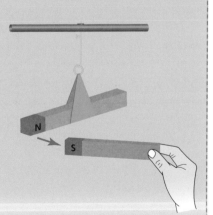

Mandatory experiment

To plot the magnetic field of a bar magnet

Procedure

1. Place a glass sheet (or cardboard) over a bar magnet.
2. Sprinkle iron filings on the glass.
3. Tap the glass gently.

Glass

Pattern made by iron filings

Result

The iron filings are arranged in a pattern, as shown.

Conclusion

The space around which a magnet exerts a force is called its magnetic field.

The earth's magnetic field

A compass, which is a small bar magnet, always points in the same direction. This happens because the earth acts like a giant bar magnet.

key point

The space around which a magnet exerts a force is called its **magnetic field**.

The north pole of a bar magnet always points along a north–south line. The earth's magnetic south pole attracts the north pole of all freely suspended magnets.

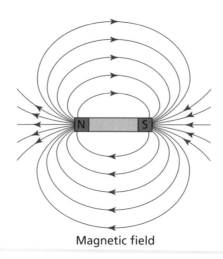

Magnetic field

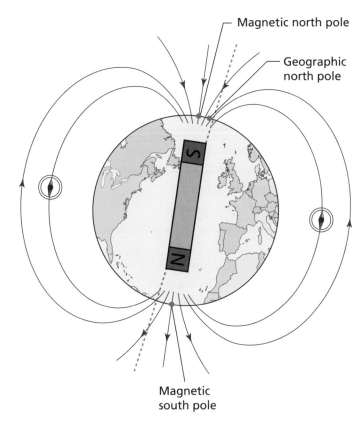

Magnetic north pole

Geographic
north pole

Magnetic
south pole

The earth's magnetic poles are not exactly the same as the geographical north and south poles, but are some distance apart. This must be taken into account when using a compass.

Sample questions and answers

1. *Which substances can be magnetised?*

Answer

Iron, steel, cobalt and nickel.

2. *Using a labelled diagram, describe how to plot the magnetic field of a bar magnet.*

Glass

Pattern made
by iron filings

Answer

(i) Place a glass sheet (or cardboard) over a bar magnet.

(ii) Sprinkle iron filings on the glass.

(iii) Tap the glass gently.

(iv) The iron filings are arranged in a pattern, as shown.

(v) The space around which a magnet exerts a force is called its magnetic field.

32 Static Electricity and Current Electricity

aims | **In this chapter you need to learn:**

1. Static electricity is produced by friction.
2. Attractive and repulsive forces exist between charged objects.
3. Earthing removes static charges.
4. An explanation of a simple circuit.
5. Mandatory experiment: To test electrical conduction in a variety of substances.
6. The differences between series and parallel circuits.
7. Mandatory experiment: To measure current, voltage and resistance and establish the relationship between them.
8. Calculations using Ohm's law.
9. Electricity in the home.
10. Calculations on power.
11. Effects of electricity.

Static electricity

key point

Static electricity is non-moving electricity. Static electricity is produced by friction.

exam focus

To generate static electricity

Procedure
Comb your hair and then hold the comb close to a small piece of paper.

Result
The piece of paper will stick to the comb.

To demonstrate the force between charged objects and the effect of earthing

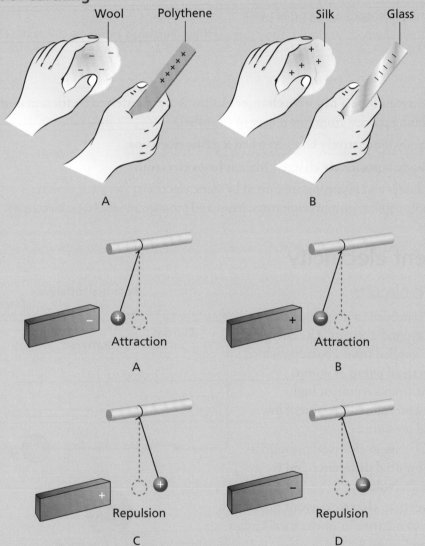

Procedure

1. Put a positive charge on a polythene rod by rubbing it with wool.
2. Charge another rod in the same way. Hold it close to the first rod.
3. Note what happens. Note what happens when you hold them in your hands.
4. Put a negative charge on a glass rod by rubbing it with silk.
5. Charge another rod in the same way. Hold it close to the other glass rod.

6. Note what happens. Note what happens when you hold them in your hands.
7. Bring a negative glass rod close to a positive polythene rod.
8. Note what happens. Note what happens when you hold them in your hands.

Results

1. Like charges repel each other.
2. Unlike charges attract each other.
3. When the rods are held, they are earthed. Earthing removes the static charge.

- **Electrons have a negative charge:** Electrons are transferred by friction during the rubbing process from one object to the other.
- A body is **negatively** charged when it **gains electrons**.
- A body is **positively** charged when it **loses electrons**.
- Thunder and lightning are caused by static electricity between clouds. Photocopiers, dust precipitators, paint and crop sprays use static electricity.

Current electricity

Simple circuits

Energy is needed to move electrical charges around a circuit. The energy is usually supplied from a **battery**, which is an electrical pump. It pumps electrons from a region of high electrical pressure to a region of low electrical pressure.

The difference in electrical pressure is called **potential difference** and is measured in **volts**.

By convention, **electric current** flows from positive to negative in an electrical circuit.

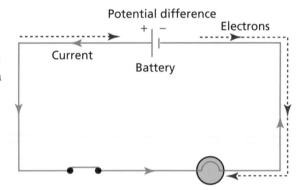

Electricity will flow in the circuit if there is a complete circuit and potential difference.

Conductors and insulators

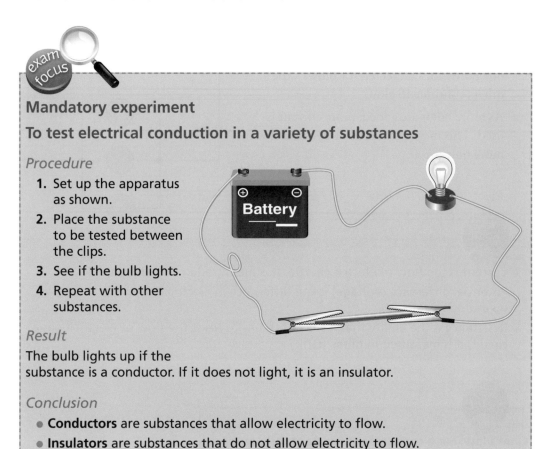

Mandatory experiment

To test electrical conduction in a variety of substances

Procedure

1. Set up the apparatus as shown.
2. Place the substance to be tested between the clips.
3. See if the bulb lights.
4. Repeat with other substances.

Result

The bulb lights up if the substance is a conductor. If it does not light, it is an insulator.

Conclusion

- **Conductors** are substances that allow electricity to flow.
- **Insulators** are substances that do not allow electricity to flow.

Series and parallel circuits

Series circuits

- Bulbs connected in series are connected one after another.
- The bulbs light because they resist the flow of electricity through the circuit. The more resistance in a circuit, the more current will flow.
- As more bulbs are connected, the light gets dimmer as the current gets smaller. If one bulb is disconnected, the circuit is broken.

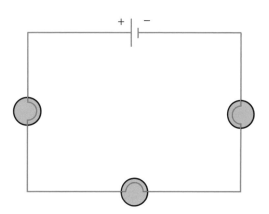

Parallel circuits

- Bulbs connected in parallel are connected side by side.
- Bulbs are brighter in a parallel circuit. When one bulb is disconnected (or blows), the others continue to glow.
- As more bulbs are added, more current is used. This means that the battery runs down more quickly.

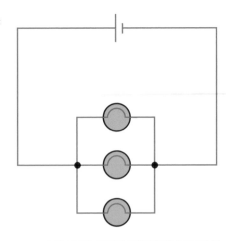

key point

- **Current** is the flow of electric charge. It is measured in **amperes** (A).
- **Potential difference (voltage)** is the difference in electrical pressure. It is measured in **volts** (V).
- **Resistance** is the ability that a substance has to resist the flow of electricity in a circuit. It is measured in **ohms** (Ω).

key point

Ohm's law: For a conductor at constant temperature:

$$\text{resistance} = \frac{\text{voltage}}{\text{current}} \quad \text{or} \quad R = \frac{V}{I} \quad \text{or} \quad V = I \times R$$

Example

What is the voltage when a current of 0.5 amps flows through the three resistors connected in series?

Total resistance:

$R = R_1 + R_2 + R_3$
$\quad = (3 + 4 + 5) \text{ ohms}$
$\quad = 12 \text{ ohms}$

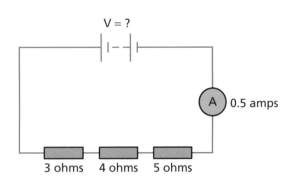

$V = I \times R$
$V = 0.5 \text{ amps} \times 12 \text{ ohms} = 6 \text{ volts}$

Symbols for circuits

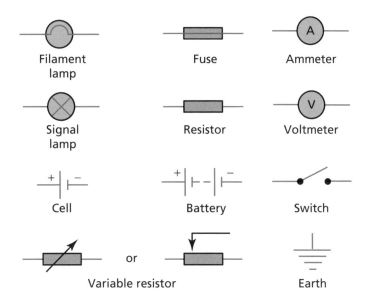

Filament lamp   Fuse   Ammeter

Signal lamp   Resistor   Voltmeter

Cell   Battery   Switch

Variable resistor   or   Earth

exam focus

Mandatory experiment

To measure current, voltage and resistance and establish the relationship between them

Procedure

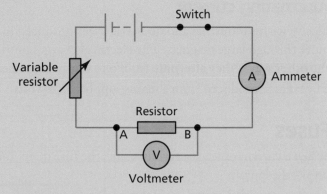

1. Set up the apparatus as shown.
2. Close the switch.
3. Read the current from the ammeter.
4. Read the voltage from the voltmeter.
5. Connect an ohmmeter (digital multimeter) from A to B and read the resistance.
6. Adjust the variable resistor. Read the current, voltage and resistance.
7. Repeat step 6 several times.
8. Plot a graph of voltage against current.

Results

Voltage (volts)	0	2	4	6	8	10
Current (amps)	0	0.5	1	1.5	2	2.5

$$\text{resistance} = \frac{10 \text{ volts}}{2.5 \text{ amps}} = 4 \text{ ohms (constant value)}$$

Conclusion

Ohm's law is verified.

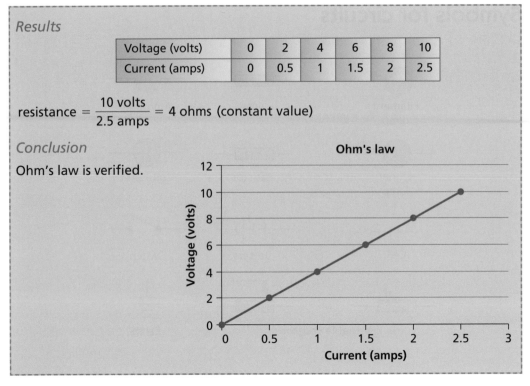

Ohm's law

Electricity in the home

Electricity in the home

Direct current

Electricity that moves around a circuit in **one direction only** is direct current.
In a simple circuit (see p. 192), the electricity flows from the positive pole in the battery through the circuit and back to the negative pole.

Alternating current

Electricity for industrial and domestic use is produced in power stations by turbines that move through large magnets. The electrical charges produced flow **one way and then the other way** – they **alternate** from one way to the other.
The voltage produced from a mains supply is 230 volts.

Fuses

When a current exceeds a certain value, the fuse melts and breaks the circuit.
Appliances with 3 amp fuses include televisions, radios, bedside lamps, etc. The fuse used should always be greater than the correct current, but as close to it as possible.
The fuse should always be connected to the live wire.

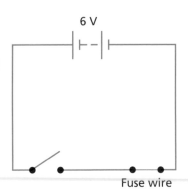

6 V

Fuse wire

Plugs

The live wire is brown and is connected to the fuse. The neutral wire is blue, while the earth wire is green and yellow.

The fuse should always be connected to the pin that takes the incoming current.

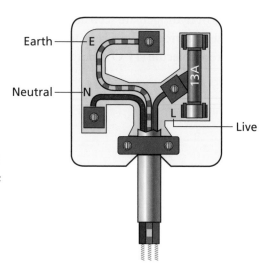

Lighting circuit

Lights are connected in parallel. If one light is switched off or blows, the others continue to light.

The live and neutral wires form a loop. The earth wire also forms a loop. No current should flow in the earth wire unless a fault develops.

Power

Power is measured in watts. The electricity provider charges a fee for the number of kilowatts used per hour.

kilowatt hours = kilowatts × hours

The number of units of electricity used by a 2 kilowatt heater in 5 hours
= 2 kilowatt × 5 hours = 10 kilowatt hours = 10 units.

Cost

The cost of using five 100 watt bulbs for 12 hours at a cost of 8 cent per unit = 5 × 0.1 × 12 × 8 c = 48 c.

Effects of electricity

Heating effect

The filament heats up and the bulb lights.

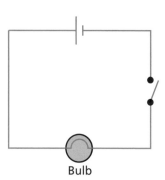

Bulb

Magnetic effect

The compass needle deflects, showing that there is a magnetic field around the wire.

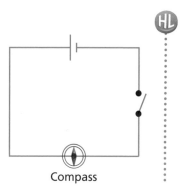

Compass

Chemical effect

Bubbles of hydrogen are seen at one electrode and bubbles of oxygen are seen rising at the other electrode. Twice as much hydrogen as oxygen is produced. This occurs because the water molecule (H_2O) contains two hydrogen atoms and one oxygen atom.

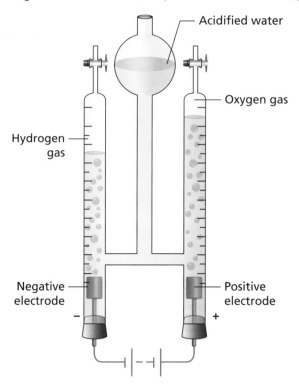

Sample questions and answers

1. *If a bulb blows in the circuit shown below, does the next bulb stay on? Give a reason for your answer.*

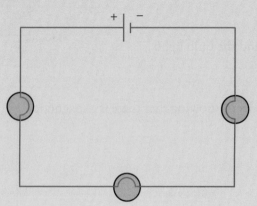

Answer

No. The circuit is broken.

2. *If a bulb blows in the circuit shown below, does the next bulb stay on? Give a reason for your answer.*

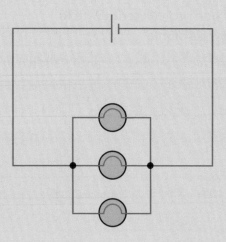

Answer

Yes. The circuit is not broken.

3. *Calculate the cost of running an electric heater with a power rating of 2 kW for 3 hours if a unit of electricity costs 12.5 c.*

Answer

cost = power (in kW) × hours × unit cost

    = 2 kW × 3 hours × 12.5 c per kW hour

    = 75 c

4. *A pupil used the circuit below to get a set of readings from both meters for different values and then plotted the data in the graph shown. (Junior Cert 2007, Q9b)*

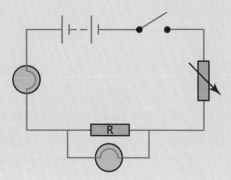

(a) *Enter A and V in the appropriate circles for ammeter and voltmeter.*
Answer
A: On left-hand side circle (in series with R).
V: On circle below resistor R.

(b) *Use the graph to calculate the resistance R shown in the diagram.*

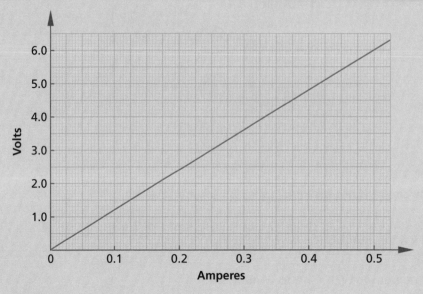

Answer

$$R = \frac{V}{I} = \frac{1.2 \text{ volts}}{0.1 \text{ amps}} = 12 \text{ ohms}$$

33 Electronics

In this chapter you need to learn:

1. Symbols for electronic devices.
2. Diodes can be forward biased or reverse biased.
3. LEDs and LDRs in circuits.

Electronic devices are used in practically every piece of electrical equipment, such as computers, dishwashers, CD players, alarms, etc. They allow small amounts of current to control devices.

Symbols

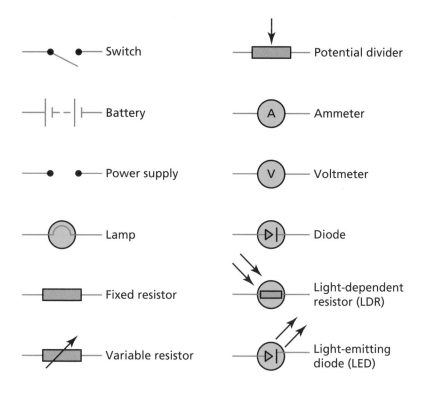

Switches

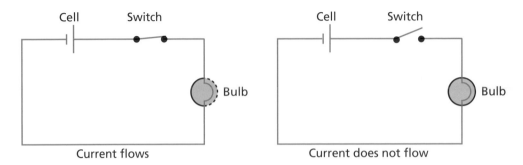

- When the switch is closed, the circuit is complete and current flows.
- When the switch is open, the circuit is not complete and no current flows.

The diode in a circuit

LED

Flat edge

Short wire (−ve)

Long wire (+ve)

Anode   Cathode
  +   −
        Symbol

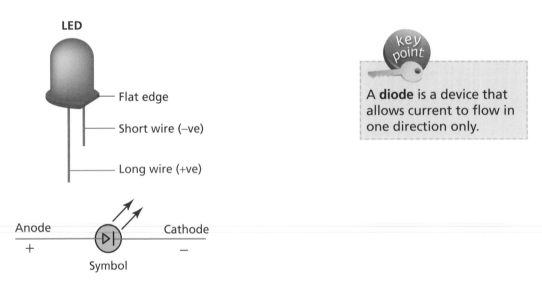

> **key point**
>
> A **diode** is a device that allows current to flow in one direction only.

When the diode is in **forward bias**, it has low resistance and allows current to flow. The bulb lights.

6 V   Forward bias

+ of battery connected to + of diode

Bulb lights

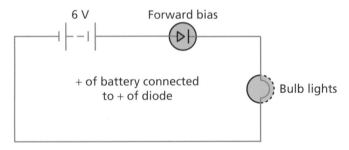

When the diode is in **reverse bias**, it has a high resistance and does not allow current to flow. The bulb does not light.

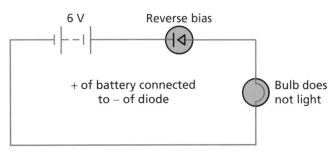

6 V   Reverse bias

+ of battery connected
to − of diode

Bulb does
not light

Light-emitting diodes in a circuit

A light-emitting diode (**LED**) is a diode that gives out light when a current flows through it.

A resistor (330 Ω) is connected in series with it to prevent it from being damaged by too great a current.

LEDs are used in clocks, radios, calculators, etc. to indicate whether they are on or off.

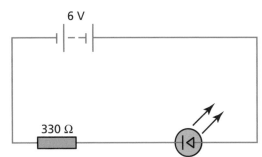

6 V

330 Ω

Water level detector

When the water rises and touches the ends of the wires, the circuit is completed and the LED lights. A buzzer can be used instead of the LED.

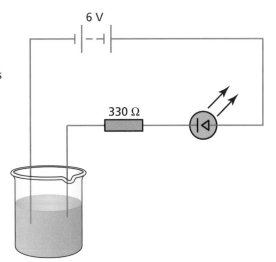

6 V

330 Ω

Light-dependent resistor (LDR)

An **LDR** is a resistor whose resistance changes when the amount of light falling on it changes. The resistance decreases when the amount of light increases. The resistance increases when the amount of light decreases.

LDRs are used to control street lighting and as light meters in cameras.

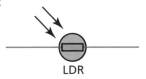

LDR

To measure the resistance of an LDR for varying degrees of brightness

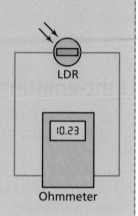

LDR

10.23

Ohmmeter

Procedure

1. Connect an LDR to an ohmmeter (or multimeter).
2. Note the resistance.
3. Change the amount of light shining on the LDR by covering it with a cloth.
4. Note the resistance.
5. Shine a bright light on the LDR.
6. Note the resistance.

Result

The resistance decreases as the light increases.

Sample question and answer

1. *Describe an experiment, using a labelled circuit diagram, to measure the resistance of an LDR under varying degrees of brightness of light. (Junior Cert 2009, Q8b)*

Answer

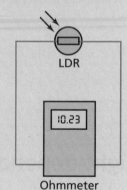

LDR

10.23

Ohmmeter

   (i)   Connect an LDR to an ohmmeter (or multimeter).
   (ii) Note the resistance.
   (iii) Change the amount of light shining on the LDR by covering it with a cloth.
   (iv) Note the resistance.
   (v)   Shine a bright light on the LDR.
   (vi) Note the resistance.
   (vii) The resistance decreases as the light increases.